The
First
Frigates

Orpheus of 1780, contemporary model.

This quarter view reveals the transoms which formed the basis of a round tuck stern. The stepping line of the after cant frames has become a curved bearding line on this model.

The First Frigates

Nine-pounder & Twelve-pounder
Frigates 1748-1815

Robert Gardiner

Illustrated with draughts from the collections of
the National Maritime Museum, Greenwich

CONWAY
MARITIME PRESS

First published in Great Britain in 1992 by
Conway Maritime Press Ltd,
101 Fleet Street,
London EC4Y 1DE

British Library Cataloguing-in-Publication Data
  Gardiner, Robert
    The First Frigates: Nine and Twelve-pounder Frigates 1748-1815
    I. Title
    623.8254

  ISBN 0 85177 601 9

Designed by Tony Garrett

Printed and bound in Great Britain by the Bath Press

Contents

Introduction

This is the first volume of a series intended to provide design histories of a range of ship types that have never been accorded detailed attention in published works. The subject for each volume will be broad enough to reflect genuine historical importance, but narrow enough to allow an in-depth study of the type. This book, for example, deals with the introduction of a vastly superior cruising ship, the frigate, in the mid-eighteenth century, but is confined to the first two generation of ships, which happens to include all those armed with 9pdr and 12pdr guns. Later and larger frigates are a separate story and could well form a subsequent volume in the series.

The work falls into two halves. The first is an outline of the background conditions and, wherever possible, the design criteria for each class – although very little discussion of cruising ship design survives from the eighteenth century, if indeed it was ever committed to paper. For the smaller ships even a proper listing by classes is not readily available in published form, so specification tables with 'design' and 'as completed' dimensions, armament and building dates are a major feature of the early chapters.

Part II is an analysis and evaluation of various general aspects of the ships themselves, once again including tabular information that is difficult to obtain elsewhere. Some sections, like those on fittings or masting and rigging, will be of particular interest to modelmakers, but others are of wider significance: the chapters on sailing qualities and comparative naval architecture offer evidence that questions the traditional view of the inferiority of British ship design in this period, for example. Furthermore, although the Royal Navy forms the core of this study, the ships of its French, Spanish, American and Dutch opponents have not been forgotten; they were always of interest to the British and often influential, so enough information survives to treat frigate design in a proper international context.

Both parts are illustrated chiefly from the incomparable collection of plans at the National Maritime Museum, Greenwich. These are prime sources of documentation on most ship types and often the only objective guide to the appearance of vessels before the age of photography. Outside the world of the dedicated specialist the draughts are little known and consequently under-valued, but an incidental aim of this series will be to reproduce as many as possible and to list others of relevance, since the Museum can provide copies in various forms for modelmaking or study purposes.

Acknowledgements

This book is the product of nearly twenty years of spare-time study, so naturally as an author my debt to individuals and institutions is broad. In Britain, thanks are due to the staff of the Public Records Office at Chancery Lane and Kew; and to various departments of the National Maritime Museum, particularly David Topliss and his predecessors in the Draught Room, the archival and library staff, and David Spence of Reprographics. In Denmark, Hans-Christian Bjerg made time in a busy schedule to provide an extremely useful introduction to the fascinating collection of plans at the Rigsarkivet in Copenhagen; archivists at Sweden's Sjöhistoriska Museum were equally helpful regarding the Chapman Collection, while this extremely valuable visit to Scandinavia was completed by the unstinted assistance of the Krigsarkivet staff in Stockholm. I have been particularly fortunate in that the nature of my work at Conway Maritime Press has inevitably introduced me to the most knowledgeable of the present generation of ship historians. It would be impossible not to benefit from frequent, often detailed, and occasionally heated discussions with fellow enthusiasts like Frank Fox, Andrew Lambert, Brian Lavery, Roderick Stewart or David White, to name but a few. However, although it may come as a surprise to them, I have been equally influenced by writers like David K Brown and Norman Friedman who may profess little interest in the era of sail but whose sophisticated analytical approach to ship design seems as valid for sailing vessels as for their powered successors.

Finally, my greatest individual debt is undoubtedly to David Lyon, for many years responsible for the plans collection at Greenwich. He has freely shared his incomparable knowledge of the Admiralty Collection, supplied endless pages of his great manuscript list of the sailing navy, and acted as a resonant sounding board over the years for many of the ideas in the pages that follow. Quite simply, his willingness to open the Draught Room on Saturdays to weekday wage-slaves made this book possible.

Needless to say, any mistakes are all my own work.

Robert Gardiner

Part I: Design History

1. The State of Cruiser Design, c1740

Like many a nation before and since, Britain went to war with Spain in 1739 militarily ill-prepared for the conflict. The long period of peace and growing prosperity had suffered no major interruption since the Treaty of Utrecht concluded hostilities with France in 1713, and although the Royal Navy had seen some action during this time, in general the strictest principles of peacetime economy had been enforced. Additional ships were virtually impossible to obtain, although decayed and worn-out vessels were replaced by new construction or 'rebuilding', a process that often amounted to the same thing.[1] Furthermore, the Establishment of 1719 fixed the dimensions and scantlings of all the rated ships down to those of 20 guns, so radical innovation was impossible. Not surprisingly, most naval historians see this as a period of technical stagnation and administrative torpor.

As far as the smaller craft are concerned, this is not entirely true,[2] although it has to be admitted that some of the development was in the wrong direction. The standard small cruiser was the 20-gun Sixth Rate, a two-decked ship that originally carried all its 6pdr guns on an open upper deck; above it, there was only a light forecastle platform, while the roof of the great cabin formed a short quarterdeck. The lower deck was fitted for rowing, with a tier of ports for long sweeps, and a larger

Gibraltar of 1727, design sheer & profile draught, dated 12 April 1727.

The 20-gun Sixth Rates of the 1719 Establishment had very light upperworks as originally conceived. The forecastle was little more than a platform, while the quarterdeck was formed of the roof over the captain's cabin; neither had rails or bulwarks and there were no gangways. However, they were genuine two-decked ships, working their cables, pumps and sweeps on the lower deck, being derived directly from the 32/36-gun Fifth Rates of the 1690s but with the upperworks radically reduced. Apart from the sweep ports, the only opening on the lower deck was a small ballast port amidships; later ships retained this even after genuine gunports were added.
(Rigsarkivet, Copenhagen)

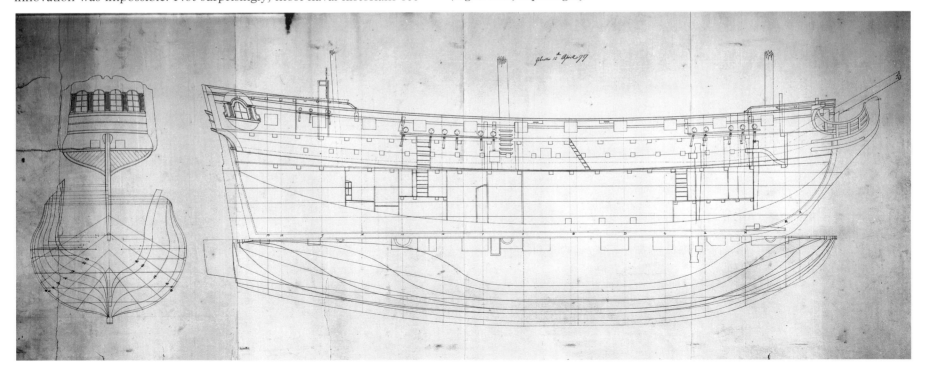

port amidships used to load ballast.[3] Ships were still designed by the Master Shipwrights of the Dockyards, which allowed a degree of variety in hull form, while the process of rebuilding offered further opportunities to stray from the strict letter of the Establishment. In general, there was a tendency for the 20s to acquire extra upperworks (higher bulwarks and a longer quarterdeck), while a pair of gunports a side was added to the lower deck aft; these changes were formalised in the 1733 modifications to the Establishment, along with a slight increase in dimensions, but before long the armament was increased to twenty-two 9pdrs (two on the lower deck) plus two 3pdrs on the quarterdeck, making them 24-gun ships. Needless to say, none of these alterations improved their sailing abilities.

There was no obvious apprehension about going to war against Spain with such vessels, although they benefited from the further general increase in dimensions proposed in 1741. Spain was geographically less well placed than France to pursue the *guerre de course* and, indeed, was confidently expected to prove the victim of a war on trade rather than its beneficiary. Spanish line of battleships impressed their opponents with their sheer size,[4] but there is no suggestion that her cruisers were at all favoured – not a single captured vessel was taken into service for cruising duties, and none was noted for its sailing qualities. The war did not go as well as the trading community hoped, but in the early years British merchant ship losses were restricted to bearable numbers, so there was only a muted agitation for improved protection.

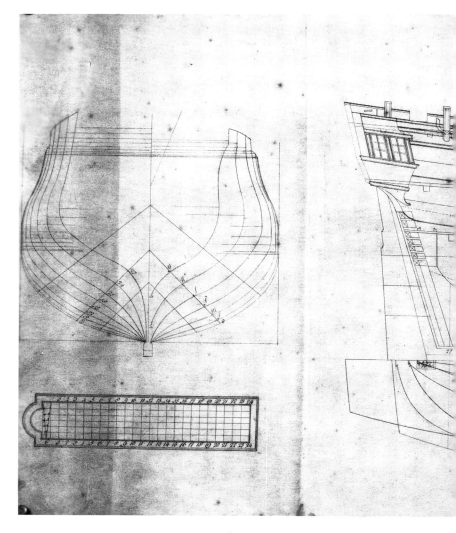

24-gun Sixth Rate of the 1745 Establishment, contemporary model.

Although the Sixth Rates were increased slightly in size at each successive Establishment, it was not enough to prevent their sailing qualities deteriorating under the additional weight of upperworks and armament. The 1745 ships, with their full-length quarterdeck, were especially poor, and provoked the crisis in cruiser design that led to the introduction of the 'frigate form' into the Royal Navy.

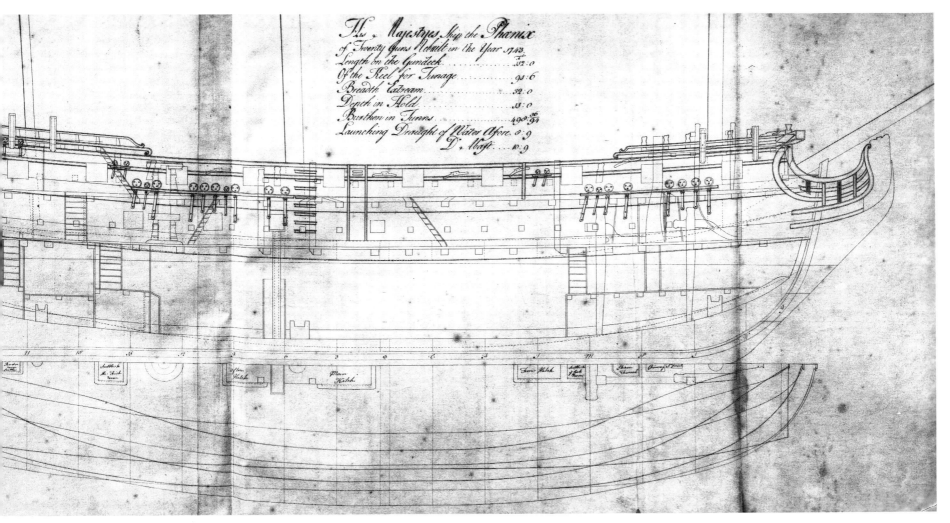

His Majestyes Ship the Phoenix
of Twenty Guns Rebuilt in the Year 1743.
Length on the Gundeck 112:0
Of the Keel for Tunage 94:6
Breadth Extream 32:0
Depth in Hold 11:0
Burthen in Tunns 490 36/94
Launching Draught of Water Afore . . . 8:9
D.º Abaft . . . 10:9

Phoenix of 1743, as fitted sheer & profile draught.

In succesive modifications to the Establishment the Sixth Rates acquired more and heavier guns and extended upperworks. Compared with 1719 ships, this 1741 Establishment 24-gun ship has two gunports a side added on the lower deck (although a gun was allocated to only one of them), and an extended forecastle and quarterdeck, the latter fitted for both carriage guns and swivels. However, the introduction of a full quarter gallery (in lieu of a quarter badge) and a beakhead instead of the round bow – both 'big ship' features – suggest their promotion in the minds of the Navy Board to more significant warships than their sloop-like predecessors.
(The Science Museum, London)

All this changed dramatically with French entry into the war in 1744. Mercantile captures shot up almost four-fold,[5] and the resulting clamour from the shipping interest forced the Admiralty to reconsider not only its convoys and cruiser policy, but also the nature of the ships themselves. Before long it became apparent that the Sixth Rates were outclassed by faster sailing French vessels, both privateers and national warships, and as the fortunes of war placed some of these ships in British hands, the Admiralty began to take a technical interest in design that had been traditionally the prerogative of the Navy Board. The Admiralty was nominally the senior body, laying down policy to be executed by the other, but during the period of the Establishments there had been little need for direction from above on matters of ship design and the Navy Board did not expect 'interference' on matters of detail. Compared with the politically appointed and somewhat ephemeral membership of the Admiralty, the Navy Board was the permanent bureaucracy of the service, and its long experience and knowledge of precedents provided much of the design continuity. It was also responsible for administering the Navy's budget and so was particularly alert to the cost implications

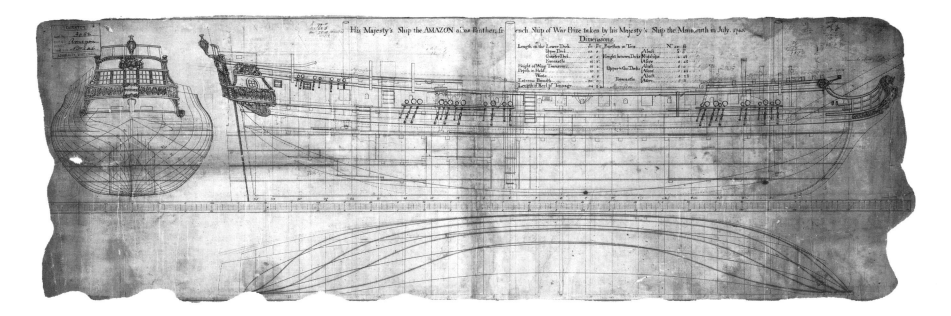

His Majesty's Ship the AMAZON allies Panther, fr[en]ch Ship of War Prize taken by his Majesty's Ship the Monmouth in July. 1745.

Dimensions.

Amazon, ex-French *Panthère*, sheer & profile draught as captured 1745.

Apart from privateers, the first French frigate-form ship captured was the 6pdr-armed *Panthère*. A greater contrast with the British Sixth Rates would be difficult to imagine: with only 4ft between decks, she was very low and the quarterdeck and forecastle had virtually no protection whatever. The ship had a fine reputation in the Royal Navy and the lines were still being used for sloops designed as late as the Napoleonic Wars.

of decisions like increasing warship size. The responsibility for the material well-being of the Navy always made it inherently conservative, but at this time the tendency was exacerbated by the dominating presence of Sir Jacob Acworth. He was old, self-opinionated and outspoken, and having been Surveyor of the Navy since 1715, with effectively the final say on matters pertaining to ship design and construction, he was used to getting his own way. Luckily for the Navy, he met more than his match in George Anson, who first came to the Admiralty in 1744.

Anson, fresh from his triumphs in the Pacific, was the man of the moment and consequently wielded considerable influence, but his epic circumnavigation had also revealed the determination that would make him a formidable reformer. An immediate start was made by the appointment of a committee under Sir John Norris to investigate a complete revision of the Establishment, and in the meantime all surveys of captured French ships were forwarded by the Navy Board for Admiralty inspection. The fact that the Dockyards were instructed to look out for good sailing cruisers – possibly as a prototype – can be inferred from numerous suggestions to 'preserve the body' by taking off the lines, even where the ship herself was not recommended for purchase.[6]

There was no shortage of small French prizes, most of which were taken by more powerful ships in circumstances like heavy weather in which their superior sailing could not be used to advantage. They varied greatly in size and included privateers as well as ships of the French navy, but the most admired had a single battery with minimal superstructure; their quarterdecks and forecastles were low and fitted with only the lightest rails, producing snug and weatherly, although sometimes rather wet, hulls. This was as much a novelty in the French service as the British, for the earlier type of small French cruiser were either a cumbersome two-decker like the British 24s, or a single-decked ship with its battery too near the waterline for all-weather use.

In 1741 the innovative constructor at Brest, Blaise Ollivier, had built a new light frigate called *Medée*, in which he kept the two-decked layout but made the upper deck the structural strength deck to carry the complete armament of twenty-six 8pdrs; the lower deck was little more than a light platform and headroom was reduced to about 4ft, while the unarmed quarterdeck and forecastle eschewed barricades to reduce windage (curiously, though, like a number of French ships, there was a small poop or roundhouse on the quarterdeck). With no ports on the lower deck it was possible to position this deck at the level of the waterline, which reduced the height of topside that had made earlier two-deckers so leewardly while keeping the battery at a height that would allow them to be run out in any fighting weather.[7] Because his talent was so widely respected, Ollivier was able to champion this type of ship with great success: *Medée* became the prototype of a standard 8pdr frigate, some thirty of which were built down to 1774, while a fellow constructor under his influence, Coulomb, introduced a smaller 20-gun 6pdr version with the *Panthère* in 1744.

Modern historians have described this layout as the 'true frigate

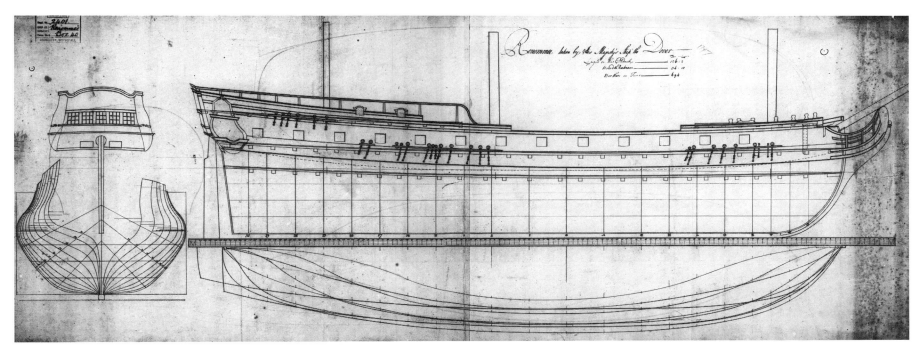

Renown, (above) ex-French *Renommée*, sheer draught as captured 1747.

Probably the fastest frigate of her day, *Renommée* was a remarkable performer in the right conditions. However, she was lightly built and had to be completely reconstructed in later life, losing her outstanding sailing qualities. Because their lines had a very fine entrance, French frigates rarely carried a gun forward of the fore mast.

Ambuscade (below), ex-French *Embuscade*, sheer & profile draught as taken off at Plymouth in August 1746.

The largest frigate-built prize of her day, the *Embuscade* was as big as a British 44, and rated as such. Her French 8pdrs were exchanged for 12pdrs in Royal Navy service and set a precedent for the British 32s and 36s of the mid-1750s; curiously, the hull form adopted for the *Unicorn*s and the *Niger*s was much closer to *Embuscade*'s than the more extreme French form of *Panthère* or *Renommée*. Note the typical French decoration of the period and the channels set below the gunports.

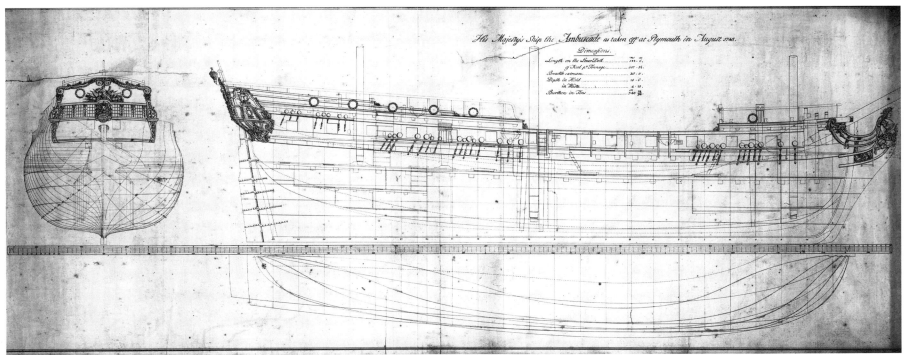

Table 1: CAPTURED SHIPS 1744-1748

Name, rate	Nationality	Built	Captured	Dimensions					Armament				Fate
				Lower deck	Keel	Breadth	Depth in hold	Burthen	Lower deck	Upper deck	Quarter-deck	Fore-castle	
				ft ins	ft ins	ft ins	ft ins	tons	(No x cal)	(No x cal)	(No x cal)	(No x cal)	
Equivalents of Sixth Rates and larger													
Grand Turk, 20 ex-24	Fr privateer	?	1745	100 9	81 10¼	81 10¼	9 5	366		18 x 9 / 22 x 9	2 x 3 / 2 x 3		1 May 1749 sold
Medway's *Prize*, 30 ex-*Favorette*, 30[1]	Fr	1743	Jan 1744	128 0		36 0	17 0	744					13 Feb 1750 sold
Lys, 24, ex-32	Fr privateer	?	Dec 1745	105 9	82 0	29 0	10 9½	366	2 x 9	20 x 6 / 22 x 6	4 x 3 / 8 x 3 & 5 swivels		13 Apr 1749 sold
Richmond, 24 ex-*Dauphin*, 24	Fr East India Co ship	1743	Jan 1746	102 0	80 0	30 6	12 6	395					28 Nov 1749 sold
Amazon, 24 ex-*Panthère*, 20	Fr	1744	Jul 1745	113 9½	84 2	31 0	10 2	481 13/94		24 x 6 / 20 x 6			Oct 1763 sold
Inverness, 24 ex-*Duc de Chartres*, 32	Fr privateer	?	18 Jan 1746	104 7	82 0	28 6	10 5	354					Oct 1749 order to BU
Ambuscade, 40 ex-*Embuscade*, 40	Fr	1745	21 Apr 1746	132 6	107 5½	36 0	11 0	746		26 x 12 / 26 x 8	10 x 6 / ?	4 x 6 / ?	9 Feb 1762 sold
Margate, 24 ex-*Leopard*, 22	Fr privateer	Bayonne, 1746	27 Oct 1746	108		31		438		22 x 9	2 x 4		7 Sep 1749 sold
Bellona, 30 ex-*Bellone*, 36	Fr privateer	Nantes, 1745	2 Jan 1747	112 3½	92 3	33 2½	10 9	541		24 x 9	4 x 4	2 x 4	2 Feb 1749 sold
Ranger, 30 ex-*Deux Couronnes*, 24	Fr privateer	?1739	5 May 1747	122 5½	98 5	34 11½	14 0½	639		24 x 9	4 x 4	2 x 4	29 May 1749 sold
Renown, 30 ex-*Renommée*, 30	Fr	Brest, 1744	27 Sep 1747	126 8	103 7	34 10½	11 8	669 53/94		24 x 9	6 x 4		May 1771 BU Woolwich

The table includes only those ships taken into British service. In many cases detailed surveys exist for other ships, including the privateers *Revenge* (398 tons) and *Tygre* (576 tons) and the French national frigates *Subtile* and *Castor* (605 tons). The armament is as fitted for British service, with the as captured armament, where known, below.

Notes:
[1] No French vessel of this name known. May be the East India Co *Favori* built at Lorient in 1744. (Her captors estimated her age at 18 months.)

form', and in the sense that most later cruisers adopted it, this is not incorrect. However, there are precedents for all of the apparently novel features of *Medée*, so it is overstating the ship's importance to describe her as the first genuine frigate.[8] That she was a significant improvement over her immediate predecessors cannot be doubted, but there were numerous privateers that exhibited similar characteristics. By a quirk of fate, *Medée* was the first prize of the war, and it is surprising that a navy desperate for small cruising ships chose not to purchase her. Although the Royal Navy was selective about privateers, virtually all other captured frigates were bought-in and her near-sister *Renommée* was very highly regarded, as was the smaller *Panthère*. Unfortunately, the kind of detailed survey that reveals so much about other French captures does not exist for *Medée*, so no critique of the vessel is possible.

While the Admiralty scrutinised surveys and reports on French ships, the Norris committee finished its recommendations. Instead of the new types urgently needed – the Admiralty was particularly keen to reduce the weight of metal for any given tonnage[9] – a rigid new Establishment of inadequately increased dimensions was promulgated in 1745. The Sixth Rates were enlarged by a meagre 10 tons, but their quarterdecks were also lengthened, producing further top weight. The *guerre de course* was intensifying and this conservatism cannot have pleased the Admiralty, so in 1747 it took an unprecedented step to achieve the desired improvement. The first 1745 Establishment ship had hardly gone to sea when in April 1747 the Admiralty ordered 'a draught to be taken of the Tyger a French privateer of 26 guns 9 pounders on one deck and 220 men, taken by the Falkland 22 Feb 1746 [1747 new style], and two ships of 24 guns to be built by it...'.

The *Tygre*, a St Malo privateer, had been captured off Ushant after a 3½-hour chase by the 50-gun *Falkland* and carried into Plymouth. Although her captor's report is not at all forthcoming about the ship, the Admiralty immediately decided to send an order to Plymouth Dockyard 'to direct the said officers to make all possible dispatch in the survey and not to suffer such delays as have been hitherto used by them in surveys of the like sort'. The precise reasons why this privateer was given such unusual priority are unknown, particularly as the survey was to point out the light, and poor quality, construction of the ship, on which basis the Admiralty decided not to purchase her.[10] However, the survey also mentions *Tygre*'s 'great character for sailing', which is probably a partial answer, but circumstantial evidence must be brought in to suggest the full story.

Anson was present at the meeting which ordered *Tygre*'s rapid survey,[11] having just come ashore after arduous winter blockade duty off Brest, where his constant complaint was the lack of cruising ships. There was a growing awareness of the qualities of the new French frigates,[12] and indeed the captured *Ambuscade* had been his best cruiser. *Falkland* was a member of his squadron, and it is possible that her captain passed on a high opinion of his prize directly to Anson, who at that very moment must have been contemplating the needs of the Western Squadron, of which he was about to take command once again. It may be speculation, but it is not unlikely that Anson felt the urgent need of a better all-weather cruiser for his newly developed strategy of year-round blockade, and was prepared to step outside the confines of the Establishment types to achieve it. To this extent the *Tygre* was perhaps little more than the right ship at the right time, but nevertheless was to hold a highly significant place in the development of British cruising ships – not only marking the first significant break with the Establishment concept but also becoming the model for the first 'frigate form' ships in the Royal Navy and many that followed after.

2. *Unicorn and Lyme, 1748*

The two new ships to the draught of the *Tygre* were obviously special. In contrast to virtually all other war-built Sixth Rates, this pair was to be set up in the Royal Dockyards, which would have to follow instructions to the letter. However, the Navy Board was known to disapprove very strongly of French methods of construction (see Chapter 12 for further details), so the Dockyards were ordered to take off the lines of the *Tygre* 'in the most exact manner' and to 'have a perfect draught drawn thereof, and to take exact account of all the scantlings, dimensions, form and manner of framing, scarphs, fastenings

Lyme of 1748, sheer & profile draught with quarterdeck and forecastle, undated but taken off after construction.

For their first essay in the frigate form, the British chose a privateer hull of less extreme proportions than the French national frigates; this became the *Unicorn* class. No plan of the *Unicorn* survives in the Admiralty Collection, although there is what is almost certainly a Navy Board original in the Chapman Collection in Stockholm. This was used as the basis for the well known illustration (Plate LV, No 10) in Chapman's famous treatise *Architectura Navalis Mercatoria* of 1768. Although not as detailed as its original, Chapman's engraving confirms the unicorn figurehead and the beakhead bow, in contrast to *Lyme*'s round bow and lion figure shown here. There were other detail differences between the ships, *Unicorn* having the aftermost quarterdeck gunport omitted and lower rails, scroll hances instead of *Lyme*'s French-style square drops at the drifts (breaks of forecastle and quarterdeck), and a two-light quarter gallery.

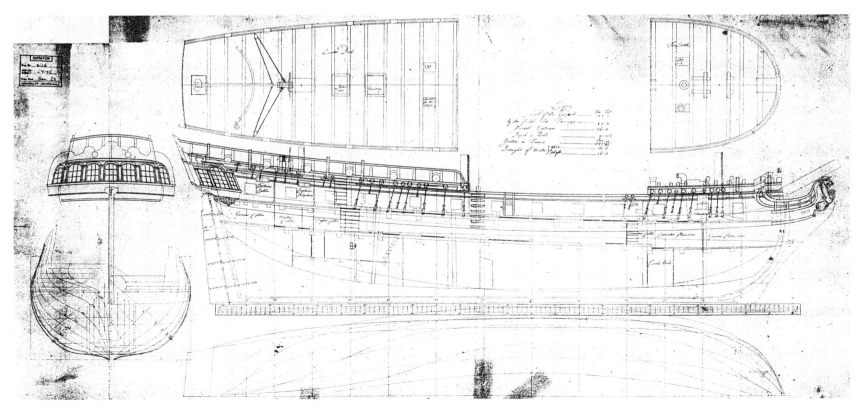

and every particular to her hull, masts and yards'; the new ships were then to be built 'without the least deviation' from this draught. One was laid down at Deptford and the other at Plymouth, the Master Shipwright at the latter yard being instructed that construction was 'to be forwarded with all possible expedition' and 'in preference to all other new works'.[13] The end of the war slowed up the pace and both ships were eventually launched in December 1748, the Plymouth ship becoming the *Unicorn* and the Deptford vessel the *Lyme*. They fully lived up to expectations, and it is significant that in his great work, *Architectura Navalis Mercatoria*, Chapman chose the *Unicorn* as the British example of a fast sailing warship.

The main characteristics of the new ships can be seen in the accompanying draughts, but it is worth pointing out the lack of headroom between decks (about 4ft) and the fact that the lower deck is well below the waterline at designed draught. This reduced the height of the side compared with the old 24s, but still gave 5ft of freeboard for the midships gunports – less than the upper deck freeboard of the earlier type but considerably more than the 2½ – 3ft of their lower deck ports. The Admiralty obviously regarded the new ships as an alternative form of 24-gun ship, and as a practical example of its belief that British ships were too small for their traditional armament. In a complete reversal of the usual development, the new ships carried two fewer 9pdrs on their upper decks than their French prototype, despite having thirteen usable ports on the broadside.

Conventional 24s of the 1745 Establishment continued to be built

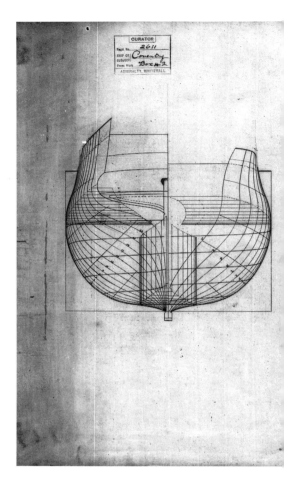

***Tartar* of 1756, design sheer & profile draught.**

Apart from additional headroom between decks the second group followed the prototypes quite closely. *Tartar* reveals the square hances and circular quarterdeck gunports that may well derive from the original French practice. The mizzen is still stepped on the lower deck, but this was to be moved to the deadwood for later ships.

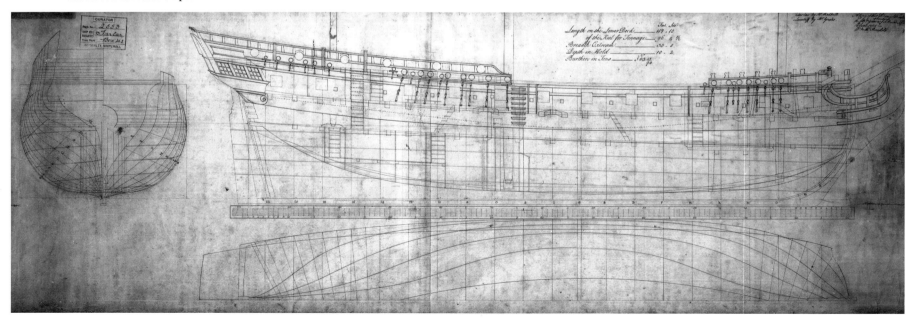

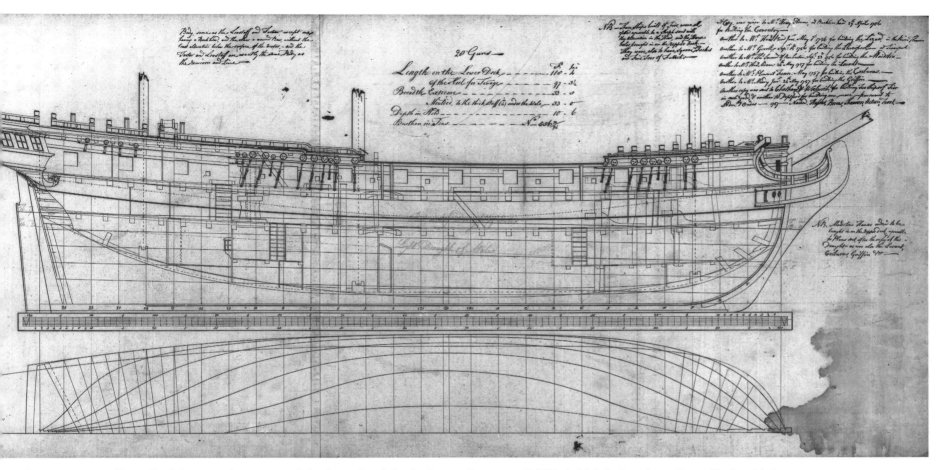

Coventry of 1757, initial design sheer & profile for third group.

but were soon discredited: because 'great complaint is made of the bad qualities of His Majesty's ships of twenty-four guns, especially with regard to their sailing', the Navy Board was instructed in October 1747 to produce an improved model. The two Surveyors[14] were both allowed to design a 24 untrammelled by the Establishment dimensions; both Allin for his *Mermaid* and Acworth for his *Seahorse* abandoned lower deck guns, and reduced the height of topside a little, but otherwise the old formula was retained. Neither ship could compare with the new frigates for sailing qualities, and with these two ships in 1749 the building of the traditional 24-gun ship ceased.

This coincided almost exactly with the death of Acworth, leaving Allin sole Surveyor, although William Bately was appointed Assistant. The Admiralty was not particularly impressed by Allin, and insisted on competitive designs for non-Establishment vessels, whereby the Master Shipwright at each dockyard produced a draught to be compared with those of the Surveyor and Assistant. In 1749 this meant designs for a small sloop for anti-smuggling duties and a new royal yacht in place of the old *Royal Caroline*. This latter ship through various rebuildings could trace its origins to the Marquis of Carmarthen's famous *Peregrine Galley* of 1700, reputedly the fastest ship in the navy in her day. Allin's winning design for the new *Royal Caroline* had a similar hull form and enjoyed

The original intentions for the third group were a radical revision of internal arrangements and topside detail, with cable handling consigned to the lower deck, although only the first three ships were so completed. This group introduced double capstans, which may have been the inspiration for the lower deck arrangement. One distinct improvement was the removal of the tiller to the lower deck, allowing the wheel to be moved forward of the mizzen and guns to be fitted where they did not threaten the shrouds or interfere with the conning of the ship (although the earlier ships had a full row of quarterdeck ports, they could not have fired guns from all of them). For the third group, the foremost broadside port was also deleted, being replaced with a chase port inside the headrails.

a favourable reputation for her sailing qualities, thus establishing a native tradition of speed under sail to contrast with designs based on French lines.

Tension with France was still high in the early 1750s and limited experimental cruiser development went ahead in anticipation of the inevitable outbreak of war. The four sloops of 1749 were built to different designs and in 1752 two additional classes to the same specification were ordered, but one employing the lines of the *Royal Caroline* and the other adapted from the lines of the captured French 74, *Monarque.* This firmly established the principle of comparative designs, with a native design competing with one of French inspiration. In this case, the *Monarque*-derived ships were adjudged relative failures, so when a new small frigate-built 20-gun ship was planned in 1753 the draughts were based on the lines of the *Royal Caroline* for one design, and a reversion to the highly successful *Tygre* for the other.[15]

By this time the Admiralty was in the process of abandoning the Establishment altogether, while *Unicorn* and *Lyme* had made themselves a fine reputation in the fleet, so as soon as the break with France seemed imminent and new frigates were needed, it was this novel class that was chosen for expansion. The first two ships, *Lowestoffe* and *Tartar* ordered in 1755, were built to 'the draught of the Lyme with such alterations as may tend to the better accommodation and carrying of guns'. However, the *Tartar* was described as 'a ship of 28 guns' and from September 1756 they were all so rated by the addition of four 3pdrs to their quarterdecks, introducing a new class and symbolising the abandonment of the Establishments for ever.

Four more slightly modified ships were ordered in 1756, the alterations being largely related to their internal fittings (see Chapter 7) and by the end of the war eighteen *Unicorn* class 28s had been added, with two stragglers completed shortly afterwards. Like most war emergency programmes, they were intended for construction in merchant yards, but an interesting exception had to be made for five ships ordered in 1757. As an experiment in the fastest possible shipbuilding, these ships were to be built of fir using a draught modified by such devices as a square tuck stern to facilitate speedy construction. The Admiralty originally wanted ten ships but the Navy Board could not get the merchant builders to make sensible tenders – some asked too much or estimated too long a construction period and some declined altogether – so eventually five were set up in the

Table 2: *UNICORN* CLASS 28-GUN SIXTH RATES
Specification

Armament:	Upper deck	Quarterdeck	Forecastle	Guns	Men
Design	24 x 9pdrs			24	160
Added by AO [Admiralty Order]					
22 Sep 1756		4 x 3pdrs		28	180
11 Nov 1756		12 x ½pdr swivels			200
10 Aug 1779 [1]		4 x 18pdr carr	2 x 18pdr carr		
2 Feb 1780		6pdrs in lieu of 3pdrs			

	Lower deck	Keel	Breadth	Depth in hold	Burthen
	ft ins	ft ins	ft ins	ft ins	tons
Tygre	118 11	96 7	33 8	11 0	576²⁴/94

FIRST GROUP 'to the lines of the Tygre French privateer'

	Lower deck	Keel	Breadth	Depth in hold	Burthen
Design	117 10	96 5½	33 8	10 2	581⁵⁰/94
As completed					
Unicorn	117 10	96 5½	33 8	10 2	581⁵⁰/94
Lyme	117 10	96 4½	33 10	9 10	587

SECOND GROUP 'to the draught of the Lyme with such alterations as may tend to the better accommodation of men and carrying of guns'

	Lower deck	Keel	Breadth	Depth in hold	Burthen
Design	117 10	96 8½	33 8	10 2	583¹³/94
As completed					
Lowestoffe	118 3	97 7³⁄₈	33 10	10 4	594
Tartar	117 10	96 11	33 9	10 3	587

Notes:
[F] Fir-built.
[1] The actual as opposed to establishment carronades, where known, are given in Table 44.

	Lower deck	Keel	Breadth	Depth in hold	Burthen
	ft ins	ft ins	ft ins	ft ins	tons

THIRD GROUP 'by the draught of the Tartar with such alterations withinboard as shall be judged necessary'

	Lower deck	Keel	Breadth	Depth in hold	Burthen
Design	118 4	97 3½	33 8	10 6	586³⁰/94
As completed					
Coventry	118 4¾	97 0½	34 0⅞	10 6	599
Lizard	118 8 ½	97 2¾	33 11	10 6	595
Liverpool	118 4	97 7¼	33 8½	10 6	590
Maidstone	118 4	97 5	33 10	10 6	593¹⁴/94
Hussar [F]	118 3	97 2½	33 8	10 5½	586⁶/94
Boreas [F]	118 5½	97 5	33 8	10 6	587³⁰/94
Shannon [F]	118 6	97 5½	33 8	10 6	587⁵³/94
Actaeon [F]	118 2¾	97 3	33 7½	10 5¾	585
Trent [F]	118 5½	97 5	33 8	10 6	587³⁰/94
Aquilon	118 7½	98 3¼	33 10¼	10 6	599
Active	118 4	97 5⅝	33 10½	10 6	594⁸⁷/94
Levant	118 5	97 3⅝	33 11	10 6	595³⁴/94
Cerberus	118 7½	97 2⅛	33 10½	10 6	593¹⁴/94
Griffin	118 4½	97 7	33 11½	10 6	598⁵²/94
Argo	118 5¾	98 1	33 11½	10 6	601⁵/94
Milford	118 3	97 5	33 9	10 6	588⁷²/94
Guadeloupe	118 4	97 3½	33 8	10 6	586³⁰/94
Carysfort	118 4	97 3½	33 8	10 6	586

MODIFIED THIRD GROUP

	Lower deck	Keel	Breadth	Depth in hold	Burthen
Laurel (design)	118 4	98 0	33 8	10 6	591
Hind	118 5	97 4	33 10	10 6	592

Table 3: UNICORN CLASS, 28-GUN SIXTH RATES
Building Data

Name	Ordered	Builder	Laid Down	Launched	Sailed	Fitted at	Fate
FIRST GROUP							
Unicorn	29 Apr 1747	Plymouth Dyd	3 Jul 1747	7 Dec 1748		Plymouth	9 Dec 1771 BU completed, Sheerness
Lyme	29 Apr 1747	Deptford Dyd	24 Sep 1747	10 Dec 1748		Deptford	18 Oct 1760 wrecked, Baltic
SECOND GROUP							
Lowestoffe	20 May 1755	Graves, Limehouse	Jun 1755	17 May 1756	8 Jun 1756	Deptford	16 May 1760 sunk in action
Tartar	12 Jun 1755	Randall, Rotherhithe	4 Jul 1755	3 Apr 1756	2 May 1756	Deptford	May 1797 wrecked, San Domingo
THIRD GROUP							
Coventry	13 Apr 1756	Adams, Beaulieu	31 May 1756	20 May 1757	31 Jul 1757	Portsmouth	10 Jan 1783 captured by French
Lizard	13 Apr 1756	Bird, Rotherhithe	5 May 1757	7 Apr 1757	1 Jun 1757	Deptford	1795 hulked; 22 Sep 1828 sold
Liverpool	3 Sep 1756	Gorill & Pownell, Liverpool	1 Oct 1756	10 Feb 1758	26 Jul 1758	Liverpool	11 Feb 1778 wrecked, Long Island
Maidstone	3 Sep 1756	Seward, Rochester	10 Oct 1756	9 Feb 1758	7 Apr 1758	Chatham	Jul 1794 BU
Hussar [F]	18 Apr 1757	Chatham Dyd	3 May 1757	23 Jul 1757	17 Aug 1757	Chatham	May 1762 captured by French, Cuba
Boreas [F]	18 Apr 1757	Woolwich Dyd	21 Apr 1757	29 Jul 1757	6 Sep 1757	Woolwich	29 Jun 1770 sold 'as useless'
Shannon [F]	18 Apr 1757	Deptford Dyd	11 May 1757	17 Aug 1757	8 Oct 1757	Deptford	30 Dec 1765 BU completed, Portsmouth
Actaeon [F]	6 May 1757	Chatham Dyd	26 May 1757	30 Sep 1757	9 Nov 1757	Chatham	9 Sept 1766 sold as unserviceable
Trent [F]	6 May 1757	Woolwich Dyd	19 May 1757	31 Oct 1757	23 Nov 1757	Woolwich	21 Jun 1764 sold as unserviceable
Aquilon	6 May 1757	Inwood, Rotherhithe	15 Jun 1757	24 May 1758	30 Jun 1758	Deptford	29 Nov 1776 sold
Active	6 May 1757	Stanton, Deptford	3 Jun 1757	11 Jan 1758	2 Mar 1758	Deptford	1 Sep 1778 capt by French
Levant	6 May 1757	Adams, Bucklers Hard	Jun 1757	6 Jul 1758	30 Mar 1759	Portsmouth	6 Jul 1780 BU completed
Cerberus	6 May 1757	Fenn, Cowes	13 Jun 1757	5 Sep 1758	11 Nov 1758	Portsmouth	7 Aug 1778 destroyed to prevent capture
Griffin	6 May 1757	Janvrin, Bursledon	Jun 1757	19 Oct 1758	13 Mar 1759	Portsmouth	14 Oct 1761 wrecked off Bermuda
Argo	19 Sep 1757	Bird, Rotherhithe	27 Sep 1757	20 Jul 1758	29 Jan 1759	Deptford	8 Nov 1776 BU completed
Milford	19 Sep 1757	Chitty, Milford Haven	Nov 1757	20 Sep 1759	28 Dec 1759	Milford	17 May 1785 sold
Guadeloupe	19 Sep 1757	Plymouth Dyd [1]	8 May 1759	5 Dec 1763	11 Jul 1764	Plymouth	10 Oct 1778 sunk to avoid capture
Carysfort	20 Feb 1764	Sheerness Dyd [2]	Jun 1764	23 Aug 1766	11 Aug 1767	Sheerness	28 Apr 1813 sold
MODIFIED THIRD GROUP							
Hind	1783	Clayton & Wilson, Sandgate	Feb 1783	22 Jul 1785	24 Nov 1787	Deptford	Jul 1811 BU at Deptford
Laurel	1783	Jacobs, Sandgate	Never				Cancelled 7 Oct 1783 [3]

Notes:

[F] Fir-built.

[1] Original builder Williams, Neyland (Pembroke) failed; order transferred 29 June 1758.

[2] 'A new ship of 28 guns in the room of the *Trent* lately sold.'

[3] Builder failed.

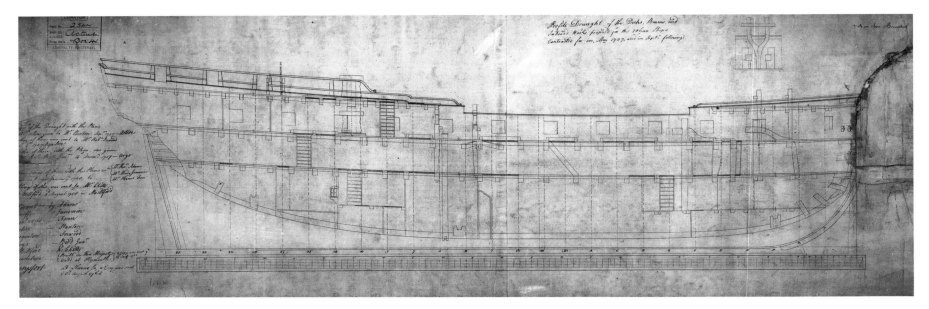

Revised profile draught for merchant-built 28s ordered in May 1757 and later.

Hawseholes on the lower deck meant that the forward storerooms had to be removed, which was achieved by installing a lower platform; this required greater depth of hull forward, which was ingeniously arranged by designing the hull to float more nearly on an even keel (the earlier ships had a very heavy drag aft). Cable handling and pumps were moved to the upper deck for all but the first three ships of the group; a note makes it clear that the draught also applied to the Dockyard-built *Guadeloupe* and *Carysfort,* while the fir-built ships were similar.

Royal Dockyards.[16] Compared with about 13 months for the normal oak-built product of a merchant yard, these vessels were launched in the staggering average time of 4 months from keel-laying and all were at sea about 5 weeks after that; *Hussar* held the record, sailing from the Medway 137 days after she was laid down. Of course, they all had short lives, but the exercise proved what could be achieved if time or seasoned timber was unavailable, and it was a tactic to be repeated in later periods of dire need.

Design sheer & profile for *Argo* and later 28s of the *Unicorn* class.

The definitive appearance of the later ships: bringing the hawseholes in on the upper deck meant moving the chase port abaft the headrails. The apparent sheer aft was also reduced, but the quarter gallery still seems too high and rather cramped in proportions.

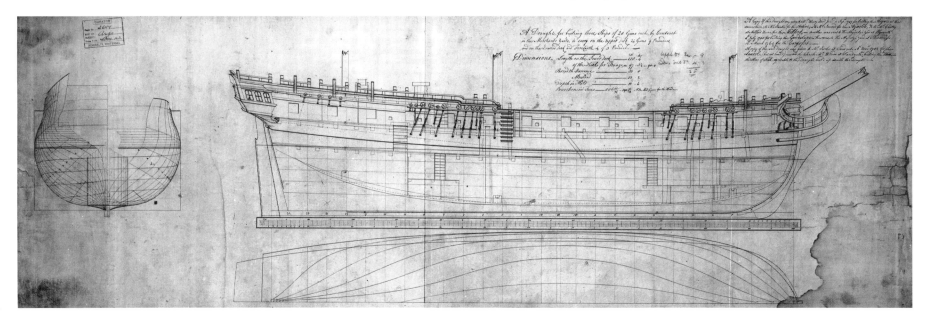

Guadeloupe of 1763, unfinished contemporary model.

Although lacking final details, the model agrees in all important respects with the *Argo* draught. At this time the forecastle and quarterdeck rails were not necessarily fitted precisely as the draught specified, but it is significant that the quarterdeck timberheads for the gun positions are exactly as indicated.

Hind of 1785, revised design sheer draught.

Although intended to be a straight copy of earlier ships, the final addition to this class showed some detail differences. The most obvious is the solid quarterdeck barricades with the enlarged carronade ports very evident (note that they are positioned so as not to threaten the shrouds with their blast); surviving ships allocated carronades would have been similarly refitted. Both bow and stern have also been altered: the higher and lighter head is a hallmark of Sir John Williams's designs, while the quarter gallery has been deepened and lowered, fairing into the sheer line with greater elegance. The final major change is the raising of the waist rail, necessary to make the gangways flush with the forecastle and quarterdeck.

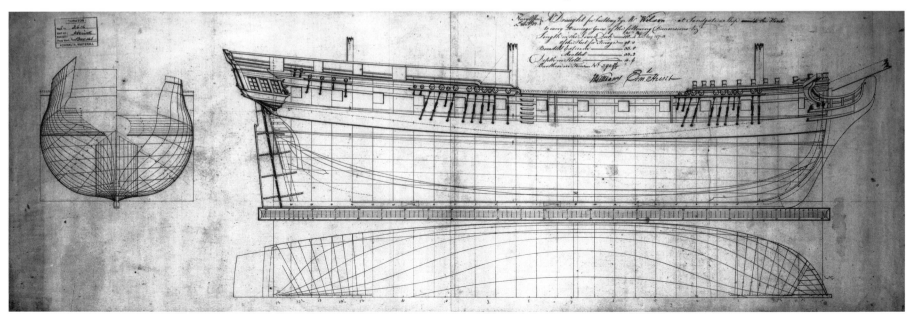

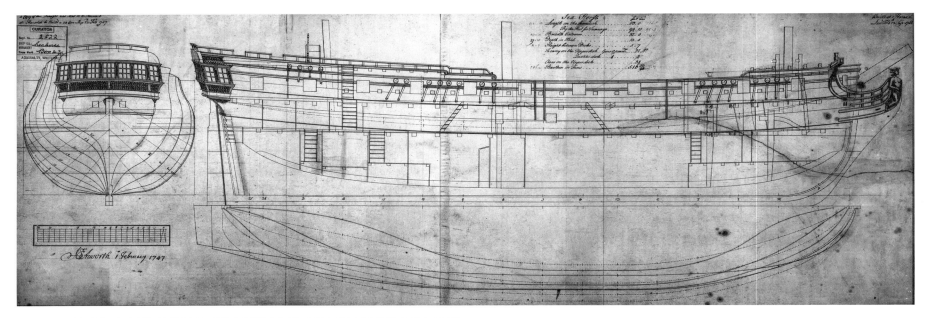

Table 4: THE RELATIVE MERITS OF THE FRIGATE AND 44-GUN SHIP

Criticism of 44-gun ships:

[...advocating building frigates in North America]

The French have for some years past built ships of war at Quebec and I have seen three of those ships at Brest, one of 60 & the others of 40 guns which were reputed to be as good ships of their rate as any of the Duke d'Anvill's squadron. Since I mention the French Navy I can't but take notice of the difference between their cruising ships and ours as to sailing, and to me it seems easy to be accounted for; the French 40 gun ships mount 30 guns, on one deck, the rest on the quarterdeck and forecastle, are great lengths & draw (little or) no more water than our 20 gun ships, are lightly timbered & every timber framed & bolted, which renders them as strong as ours, tho' loaded with timber. Our 40 gun ships have two tiers of guns, an half deck & round house upon that, which makes them lofty & consequently draw water, and of course must be bad sailers. I was taken on my passage from Jamaica by the Syren [*Sirene*[1]] frigate of war, which sails

The Navy Board's response:

Forty gun ships may undoubtedly be built slighter & much snugger than our present ships whose extra strength and height increases their weight aloft, and may thereby obstruct their sailing but their guns being on two decks gives good room for both men and guns to be much better disposed on, in action, than were they placed on one deck and a quarterdeck as proposed. The French ships are certainly much weaker ships than ours.

Our forty gun ships have not any cabins or round houses on their quarterdeck.

Seahorse of 1748, design sheer & profile draught.

Despite the obvious success of *Unicorn* and *Lyme*, the Surveyors were allowed to build competing Sixth Rates untrammelled by Establishment dimensions. This is Sir Jacob Acworth's submission, much like a 1745 Establishment ship with the lower deck gunports omitted, although reverting to the much earlier version of the round bow. As built the ship did not compare favourably with the, admittedly larger, new frigate-built ships.

infinitely better than any of our cruising ships. She is 119 feet 2 ins long by the keel, 37 ins [feet] broad & draws 13 feet 10 ins water. She is a sharp ship, the lower part of her body or rising line at or abaft the midships, a narrow floor & the extreme breadth before the midships, which makes her swim as much by the stern as on a moderate pressure she may be upon an even keel; after the same manner are all the ships of war built at Brest. I can't think what reason can be assigned for building our 40 gun ships with two tier of ports & loading them with timber for cruising ships in time of war; for tis evident to every man that understands sea affairs that they can never answer, for all ships that are not of the line of battle can answer no other end but for cruisers & being sent with dispatches on emergencies if

The French ships generally swim more by the stern than ours and draw more water.

Our forty gun ships carry a much greater weight of metal and are better ships of war, and were they built snugger & lighter timbered might sail better. Our 40 gun ships are often convoys as well as cruisers and often engaged with the enemy.

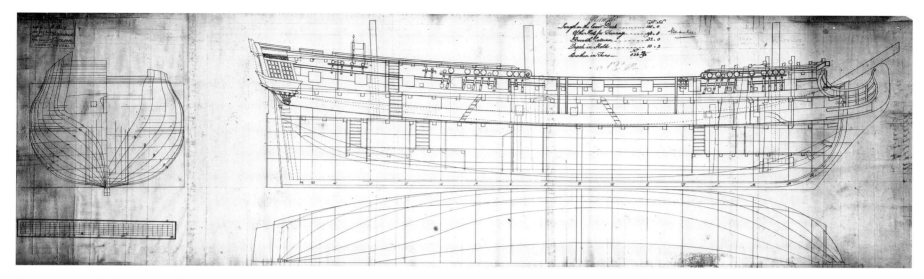

they are not good sailers the end they
are built for is not answered.

Whereas the French 40 gun ships are the
only ships that do us all the damage for
sailing better than ours, they can take
all advantages as they find the weather,
for if it blows hard that our ships can't
open their lower ports, the French ships
mounting 15 12 pounders & 5, 4 or 6
pounders[2] on each side have vastly
the advantage; nay even in moderate
weather as their men & officers are all
in sight, I can't think but those ships
have the advantage in fighting, but if
they find themselves overpowered they
can with ease make their escape.

On the whole I can't but think the
French cruisers much better ships than
ours, at least in time of war, and as
New England timber is very long and proper
for building such ships to advantage, I
conceive that a yard would be in many respects of great service to the Government
in general and more so to New England.
But if a yard should not be deemed proper
to be erected, ships might be built by
contract as good or better than any I
have seen in the West Indies, which observations I submit to the judgement of
your Lordships.

*There are many ships taken by
the French with much smaller
ships than those they have of
40 guns.*

*Most of our 40 gun ships can
open their lower tier in any
fighting weather, where they
have 20 18 pounders and they
have twenty nine pounders upon
the upper deck & 4 six pounders
on the quarterdeck that may be
used in all weather.*

*Guns & men crowded together,
most of them exposed as they
are on board the French ships,
cannot have any advantage in
fighting of a ship that has
more room for both; however,
ships may be built to carry 40
guns on one deck, quarterdeck &
forecastle which will have the
advantage of 40 gun ships with
two decks when they cannot use
their lower tier.*

*This may be of service to New
England but we fear very little
if any, to the Government in
general.*

Mermaid of 1748, design sheer & profile draught.

Although a marginally better performer under sail than *Seahorse,* Allin's
Mermaid was equally retrograde. She also gave up the lower deck ports and
reduced topside height a little, but the proportions were still tall in comparison
with the new frigates.

From a report of 15 May 1747, PRO Adm 106/2183.

Notes:

[1]*Sirène*, an 8pdr frigate built in 1744, was captured by the *Boreas* in 1760. She is the ship
depicted in Chapman's *Architectura Navalis Mercatoria*, Plate LV, along with *Unicorn.*

[2]No ships of this description were yet in service, so the correspondent was either mistaking
French 8pdrs for 12pdrs, or he had heard of the first 12pdr ships then under construction.
Since very few ever carried thirty upper deck guns of any calibre, he was probably just
mistaken – although remarkably prophetic.

3. The First 32s and 36s, 1756

In the Establishment era the standard 'heavy cruiser' was the 44-gun two-decker; like the 24, it was hampered by its high topsides, while the lower deck 18pdr battery could rarely manage 4ft of freeboard, so the ships were often reduced to their upper deck 9pdrs in weather when they could not safely open their lower ports. This was just acceptable while the French also built such ships (usually with a 12pdr main battery), but the *Junon* of 1747 was the last; in 1748 a new type of 12pdr ship was introduced with the launch of the *Hermione* at Rochefort. Nominally a frigate-built ship, she owed nothing to the sylph-like proportions of *Medée*, but the very deep hull resembled a two-decker with the lower deck unarmed (in fact, when the ship was captured in 1758, she was found to have six ports on the lower deck, although they were only employed for ventilation and ballast).

By 1756, at the beginning of the Seven Years War, there were only three 12pdr frigates in the French navy but their reputation had gone before them. As early as 1747 a report ostensibly concerned with the waste of government woodlands in North America concluded with a disparaging comparison between the new French frigates and British 44-gun ships.[17] The Admiralty requested comments from the Navy Board, and as this is the only known official statement of policy

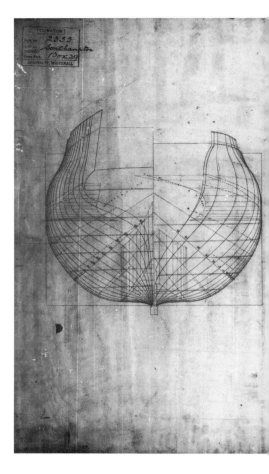

Southampton class of 1756, modified design sheer and profile draught.

The first British frigate-built Fifth Rates had some features of the two-deckers they in effect replaced. They had the lower deck cable handling originally proposed for the contemporary third group of 28s and also carried a row of sweep ports between decks. With a relatively full hull form and robustly constructed, they were good sea-boats and performed well in heavy weather but were not very fast.

regarding 44s, it is worth noting the grounds on which they were defended. The relevant paragraphs of the report are given in full in Table 4 but the significant points are that the Navy Board conceded the inferior sailing qualities of the two-deckers, but insisted that they were *better ships of war* because they carried a heavier weight of metal and did not have a large proportion of their crews exposed to enemy fire on open and lightly built upperworks; since they were as often convoy escorts as cruisers they needed to be able to fight other warships, implying that French frigates were really only commerce raiders, principally suited to action against lightly armed merchantmen. This emphasis on a tactically defensive ship is important because although the new 12pdr armed frigates were far better sailers than the old 44s, the requirement for more robust construction and greater firepower was to be perpetuated.

In 1755 Allin had become ill, and he was swiftly replaced by two

Table 5: *SOUTHAMPTON* CLASS 32-GUN FIFTH RATES
Specification

Armament:	Upper deck	Quarterdeck	Forecastle	Guns	Men
Design	26 x 12pdrs	6 x 6pdrs[1]		32	210
Added by AO					
11 Nov 1756		12 x ½pdr swivels			
10 Aug 1779		6 x 18pdr carr	2 x 18pdr carr		
25 Dec 1779[2]		4 x 18pdr carr	2 x 18pdr carr		
19 Nov 1794		4 x 24pdr carr	2 x 24pdr carr		

Designed by Sir Thomas Slade

	Lower deck	Keel	Breadth	Depth in hold	Burthen
	ft ins	*ft ins*	*ft ins*	*ft ins*	*tons*
Orig design	124 1	102 3½	34 8	12 0	648 37/94
Modified[3]	124 4	102 3½	34 8	12 0	652 51/94
As completed					
Southampton	124 4	103 1	35 0	12 1	671 64/94
Vestal	124 4	102 1½	34 10	12 10	659
Minerva	124 4	102 2¼	34 11½	12 0	664 24/94
Diana	124 6	103 1⅛	34 11	12 0	668 57/94

Notes:

[1] All 6pdrs were originally allocated to the quarterdeck.
[2] The actual as opposed to establishment carronades, where known, are given in Table 44.
[3] On 25 May 1756 the design was altered by 3in being added to the lower deck.

***Hermione*, French 12pdr frigate, design draught.**

This, the first French 12pdr frigate, was designed by the *constructeur* Morineau, who had already built the famous 74 *Invincible* four years earlier. *Hermione* was unusually deeply proportioned for a French frigate and although it is not apparent on this draught, as built the ship had a few ports on the lower deck (but none was armed). This Danish draught is probably a straight copy of the design drawing. *(Rigsarkivet, Copenhagen)*

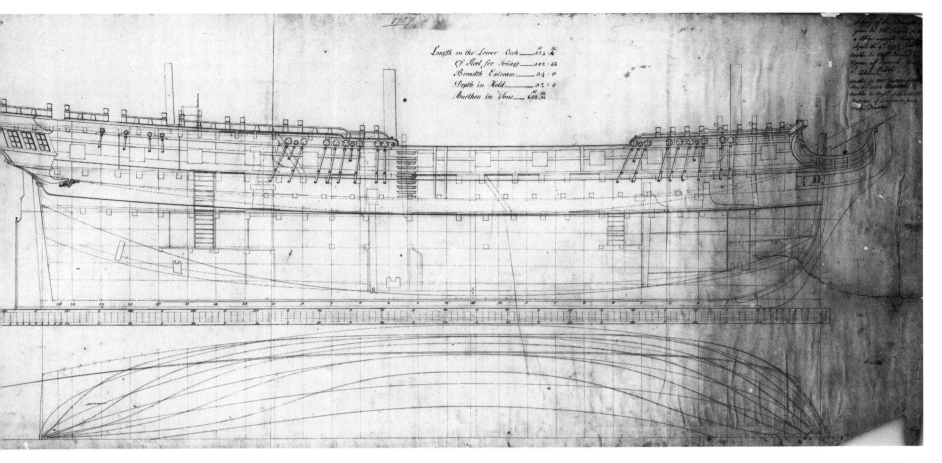

Length on the Lower Deck ___
Of Keel for Tonnage ___
Breadth Extreme ___
Depth in Hold ___
Burthen in Tons ___

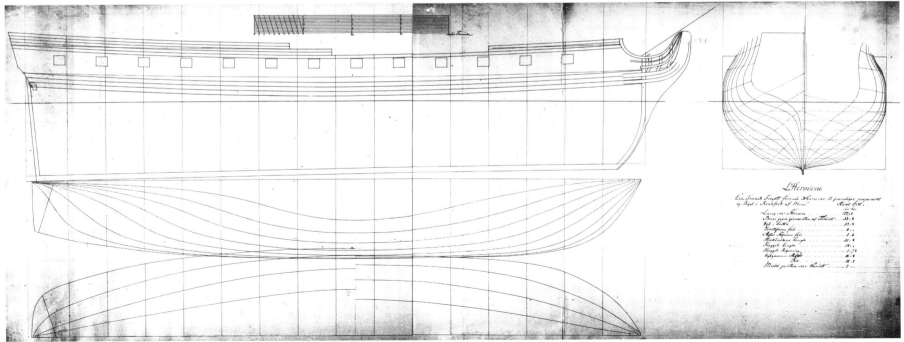

L'Hermione

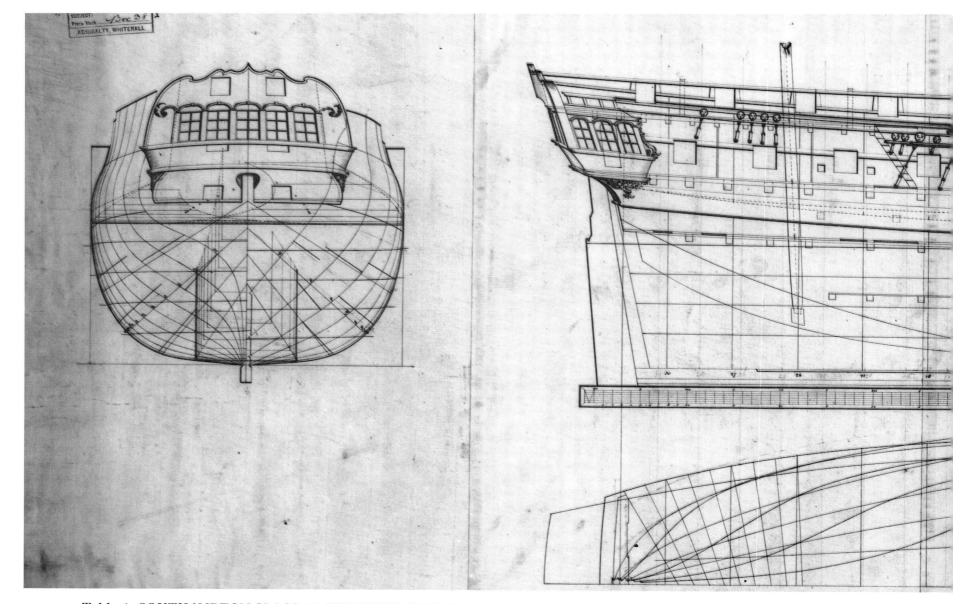

Table 6: *SOUTHAMPTON* CLASS 32-GUN FIFTH RATES
Building Data

Name	Ordered	Builder	Laid Down	Launched	Sailed	Fitted at	Fate
Southampton	12 Mar 1756	Inwood, Rotherhithe	Apr 1756	5 May 1757	19 June 1757	Deptford	27 Nov 1812 wrecked in Bahamas
Vestal	25 May 1756	Barnard & Turner, Harwich	Jun 1756	17 Jun 1757	17 Aug 1757	Harwich	1775 BU
Minerva	25 May 1756	Quallet, Rotherhithe	1 Jun 1756	17 Jan 1759	Mar 1759	Deptford	30 Dec 1784 sold
Diana	1 Jun 1756	Batson, Limehouse	Jun 1756	30 Aug 1757	12 Sep 1757	Deptford	16 May 1793 sold

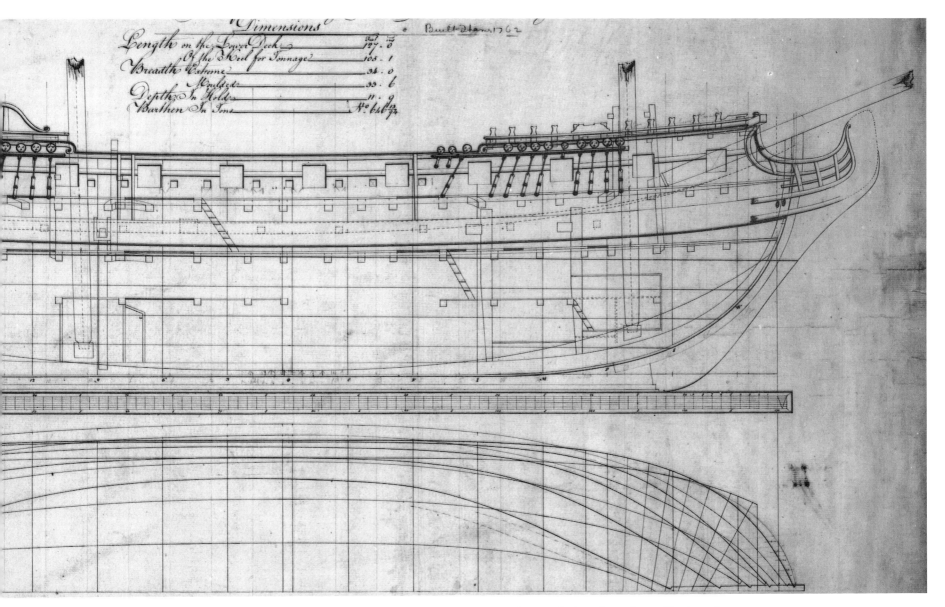

Dimensions   Built Sham 1762

Length on the Lower Deck _____ 127 . 0
Of the Keel for Tonnage _____ 105 . 1
Breadth Extreme _____ 34 . 0
Moulded _____ 33 . 6
Depth in Hold _____ 11 . 9
Burthen in Tons _____ № 646 42/94

Boston of 1762, design sheer & profile draught.

Although exhibiting the detail of an as fitted drawing, the design dimensions are quoted, suggesting that the drawing predates completion. The very different hull form from the *Southampton*s is very clear, particularly in the fore body, so aptly described by Howard Chapelle as 'scow-like'. The hull form was ultimately derived from the Marquis of Carmarthen's *Peregrine Galley* of 1700. There are small ports on the lower deck but these are probably ventilation scuttles, the oarports being definitely shown on the upper deck between the gunports.

new Surveyors, Edward Bately and Thomas Slade. The former, the existing Assistant Surveyor, was a competent but traditionally-minded man who was to be relegated to junior partner, whereas Slade became the finest British ship designer of the eighteenth century – his best known work is Nelson's immortal *Victory*, but more significantly he was responsible for a line of successful 74-gun ships and most of the early frigate designs. The appointment of Slade intensified the existing willingness to experiment and under his guidance the Royal Navy entered its most innovative period of naval architecture in the eighteenth century. Not least of his achievements was the introduction of the 12pdr armed frigate into the British service.

The Admiralty had been interested in 12pdr cruisers since at least 1746, when it had instructed the Navy Board to consider the advantages

Table 7: *RICHMOND* CLASS 32-GUN FIFTH RATES
Specification

Armament:	Upper deck	Quarterdeck	Forecastle	Guns	Men
Design	26 x 12pdrs	6 x 6pdrs[1]		32[2]	210
Added by AO					
11 Nov 1756		12 x ½pdr swivels			
10 Aug 1779		6 x 18pdr carr	2 x 18pdr carr		
25 Dec 1779[3]		4 x 18pdr carr	2 x 18pdr carr		
19 Nov 1794		4 x 24pdr carr	2 x 24pdr carr		

Designed by William Bately to the lines of the *Royal Caroline*

	Lower deck	Keel	Breadth	Depth in hold	Burthen
	ft ins	ft ins	ft ins	ft ins	tons
Design	127 0	105 1	34 0	11 9	646 ^{13}/94
As completed					
Richmond	127 1½	107 1⅛	34 1¾	11 10	664
Juno	127 10	107 0⅛	34 3	11 10	667½
Thames	127 0	104 8⅛	34 4	11 9	656 ^{46}/94
Boston	127 5	107 8	34 4½	120½	676 ^{67}/94
Lark	127 2	108 0⅜	34 5	120½	680 ^{61}/94
Jason	127 4	106 10¼	34 10	120½	689 ^{59}/94

Notes:

[1] All 6pdrs were originally allocated to the quarterdeck.

[2] *Boston* and *Jason* carried a reduced armament of 22 x 12pdrs, 4 x 6pdrs and 2 x 6pdrs with 200 men and the spars of a 28-gun ship between September 1777 and Apr 1779 (*Boston* Nov 1779).

[3] Actual as opposed to established numbers of carronades, where known, are given in Table 44.

of building Sixth Rates strong enough to carry this calibre.[18] It would have been a retrograde step because, if anything, British ships already carried too much armament for their tonnage, but the Admiralty continued to press for heavier guns. It usually suggested larger calibres for French prizes, and while the Navy Board won the argument to retain 6pdrs in the *Amazon*, ex-*Panthère* ('being not so strong built as the English 24-gun ships, her masts being taunter [taller] in proportion'), the Admiralty insisted on 12pdrs replacing the *Ambuscade*'s French 8pdrs. As the only frigate-built prize of this war to carry 12pdrs – and a highly regarded ship in the fleet – *Ambuscade* is the most likely inspiration for the first British 32- and 36-gun ships. However, despite the fact that surviving records are quite candid about the starting point for any French-derived design, there is no hint that Slade's *Southampton* (32) and *Pallas* (36) were anything but *ab initio* designs.

The sequence of events leading up to their ordering reinforces this probability. The Admiralty was disenchanted with the Establishment system, and during the early 1750s sought the Privy Council's permission to depart from its provisions for virtually every new ship. Furthermore, the Admiralty simply refused to order those Establishment types it most disapproved of, namely the three-decker 80, the 44-gun ship and the 24. This last had already been superseded by copying a French type for the *Unicorn* class, but since 1755 the new Surveyors

***Sapphire*, reduced to a 32-gun ship, 1756; proposed sheer & profile.**

The dotted line shows the original profile, and since there is no room for a second tier of ports it suggests that the new upper deck was raised from its original position; combined with the need to add one and respace the remaining gunports, the reconstruction must have involved replacing most of the topsides. In order not to have to rebuild the stern, a quarter badge (as usually applied to sloops) was adopted in lieu of a full gallery. The interior layout seems to follow that of the contemporary *Niger*s, with a magazine aft and a galley stove on the forward platform.

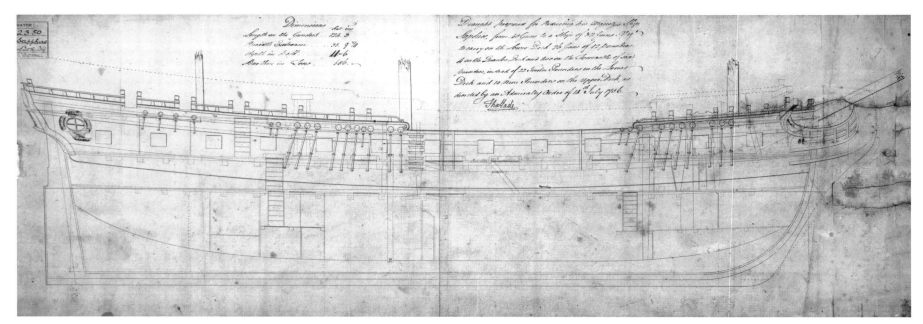

had been actively cooperating to replace the 80s with the first native-designed 74-gun ships. This left only the 44, whose logical successor was a more powerful frigate; these were not normally built in peacetime, but as soon as war broke out again in 1756, they were given a high priority, the first two 32-gun ships being ordered on 12 March.

Richmond class of 1756, contemporary model.

All the known models of 32s of this generation depict *Richmond* class ships, the most obvious difference from the *Southampton* class being an extra gunport right forward. This model lacks oarports and scuttles, but otherwise conforms closely to the design draughts.

Table 8: *RICHMOND* CLASS 32-GUN FIFTH RATES
Building Data

Name	Ordered	Builder	Laid Down	Launched	Sailed	Fitted at	Fate
Richmond	12 Mar 1756	Buxton, Deptford	Apr 1756	12 Nov 1757	7 Dec 1757	Deptford	11 Sep 1781 captured by French *Aigrette*
Juno	1 Jun 1756	Alexander, Rotherhithe	Jun 1756	29 Sep 1757	6 Nov 1757	Deptford	7 Aug 1778 burnt to avoid capture
Thames	11 Jan 1757	Adams, Bucklers Hard	Feb 1757	10 Apr 1758	29 May 1758	Portsmouth	Sep 1803 BU
Boston	24 Mar 1761	Inwood, Rotherhithe	5 May 1761	11 May 1762	16 Jul 1762	Deptford	May 1811 BU
Lark	24 Mar 1761	Bird, Rotherhithe	5 May 1761	10 May 1762	9 Jul 1762	Deptford	7 Aug 1778 burnt to avoid capture
Jason	30 Jan 1762	Batson, Limehouse	1 Apr 1762	13 Jun 1763	26 Jul 1763	Deptford	10 Feb 1785 sold

Table 9: *PALLAS* CLASS 36-GUN FIFTH RATES
Specification

Armament:	Upper deck	Quarterdeck	Forecastle	Guns	Men
Design	26 x 12pdrs	8 x 6pdrs	2 x 6pdrs	36	240
		12 x ½pdr swivels			
Added by AO 10 Aug 1779[1]		4 x 18pdr carr	4 x 18pdr carr		
Designed by Sir Thomas Slade					

	Lower deck	Keel	Breadth	Depth in hold	Burthen
	ft ins	ft ins	ft ins	ft ins	tons
Design	128 4	106 2⅝	35 8	12 4	718³⁸/₉₄
As completed					
Pallas	128 4½	106 4	35 10¾	12 4½	728⁷³/₉₄
Venus	128 4	106 3	35 9	12 4	722
Brilliant	128 4	106 2⅝	35 8	12 4	718³⁸/₉₄

Notes:

[1] Neither surviving ship carried the established number of carronades; *Venus* was reduced to a 32 in 1792 by removing two 12pdrs and two quarterdeck 6pdrs, but from 1793 had six 6pdrs but in 1793 she had six 18pdr carronades added. See Table 44.

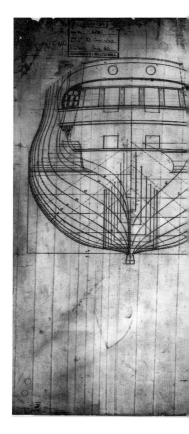

Unidentified design for large Fifth Rate.

Although not identified, stylistically the design appears to date from about 1756. There are detailed similarities with both the *Southampton* and *Pallas* classes (the four-bracket, two-rail head is a Slade trademark) and the hull form is not radically different, although the floors are not as flat. The gunport arrangement is similar to the old 1745 Establishment Sixth Rates, but the ports seem to be for the same calibre guns as those on the upper deck (probably 12pdrs). With a length of 135ft and a burthen of 793 tons and ports for 40 guns, the design may well be an attempt at a more exact replacement for the 44-gun two-decker, before it became clear that frigate-built 32s and 36s would meet the requirement.

As with the Sixth Rates, each Surveyor sponsored a design: Bately worked up his favourite *Royal Caroline* lines to produce the *Richmond*, while Slade's *Southampton* had no obvious starting point. As designed, both were a fraction under 650 tons, and so smaller than the average French 8pdr frigate, let alone the 812-ton *Hermione*, despite being intended to carry twenty-six 12pdrs on the upper deck and six 6pdrs on the quarterdeck. In general, they were proportionately shorter and deeper than French frigates, and more heavily constructed [see table 54]. Like the *Hermione*, there are hints that these ships were visualised, at least initially, as derivatives of the old two-decker 44s. There is an intriguing draught (ZAZ3180), unidentified but bearing a number of Slade hallmarks, that seems to be a larger version of his early frigate designs; this ship not only carries a ballast port on the lower deck amidships, but also two gunports a side aft on this deck as the 24-gun ships of the 1745 Establishment had done. Even if Slade eventually rejected this configuration, the ships he did build retained 6ft of head-room, which is only 8in less than that of a 1745 Establishment 44 – and not only did they work their cables and pumps on the lower deck but the *Southampton*s even had oarports there.

Three sisters for the *Southampton* and one for the *Richmond* were ordered later in 1756, along with three of a new 36-gun type that became the *Pallas* class. The initiative for the latter may have come from the Navy Board, and in particular from Slade, who was its designer. At 718 tons they were 11 per cent bigger than the *Southampton*, whose hull form they resembled, but the additional four 6pdrs increased their broadside weight by less than 7 per cent. The type may well represent an attempt by Slade to establish a larger norm for the 12pdr frigate before 650 tons could become the accepted standard, but if so he failed because no more 12pdr 36s were ever ordered. It is unlikely that this was the product of dissatisfaction with the hull form, because a revised design would have been proposed, as was about to happen with the 32s.

Although not an integral part of the development of the frigate, one

Table 10: *PALLAS* CLASS 36-GUN FIFTH RATES
Building Data

Name	Ordered	Builder	Laid Down	Launched	Sailed Fitted at	Fate
Pallas	13 Jul 1756	Wells, Deptford	Jul 1756	30 Aug 1757	8 Oct 1757 Deptford	24 Mar 1783 beached as unserviceable
Venus	13 Jul 1756	Okill, Liverpool	16 Aug 1756	11 Mar 1758	30 Jun 1758 Liverpool	1809 renamed *Heroine*; 1817 hulked; 22 Sep 1828 sold
Brilliant	29 Jul 1756	Plymouth Dyd	28 Aug 1756	27 Oct 1757	20 Nov 1757 Plymouth	1 Nov 1776 sold

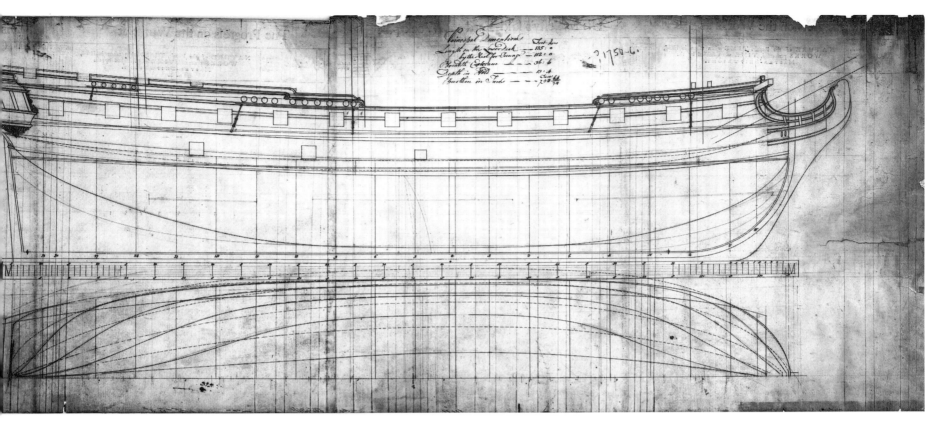

other source of 32-gun ships should be mentioned, namely the *razée*. This French term encompassed the reduction of vessels to a lower rate, usually by cutting away the superstructure and removing a complete deck. It was to become particularly popular in the early nineteenth century, with battleships reduced to frigates, and frigates to corvettes, but there are earlier precedents. In 1756 two old 44-gun ships of the 1733 Establishment, the *Adventure* and *Sapphire*, were reported to require major work and the Navy Board suggested that *Adventure* be made a 32, she 'having a better character for sailing than most of the 40-gun ships'. The Admiralty agreed and included the other ship. The initial intention was to cut away their quarterdeck and forecastle but to retain the upper deck, which would carry the reduced complement of ten 9pdrs; by filling all the lower deck ports they could be fitted with twenty-two 12pdrs.

However, defects in the *Sapphire* required the replacement of much of the topsides, which gave the dockyard the opportunity to add two extra ports to the lower deck so that the ship could be fitted as a standard 32 with twenty-six 12pdrs. A major disadvantage of most razéed two-deckers was the lack of freeboard to the lower deck ports, and with this ship it was decided to reduce displacement (and consequently increase freeboard) by lightening the upperworks to a genuine quarterdeck and forecastle. This improvement allowed the ship to be armed as a standard 32 with 6pdrs on the quarterdeck, and was extended to the *Adventure*. In as far as the razée process produced useful ships

Table 11: RAZÉE 44-GUN SHIPS (32-GUN FIFTH RATES)
Specification

Armament:	Lower deck	Upper deck	Quarterdeck	Guns	Men
As completed	20 x 12pdrs	20 x 9pdrs	4 x 6pdrs	44	250
By AO 14 Jul 1756	22 x 12pdrs	10 x 9pdrs		32	210

	Upper deck	Quarterdeck	Forecastle		
By AO 20 Jun 1758	26 x 12pdrs	4 x 6pdrs	2 x 6pdrs	32	210
		12 x ½pdr swivels			

	Lower deck	Keel	Breadth	Depth in hold	Burthen
	ft ins	ft ins	ft ins	ft ins	tons
1733 Establishment	124 0	100 3	35 8	14 6	678
As converted					
Adventure	124 3	100 3	35 10	11 6	683
Sapphire	124 3	100 6¼	35 9⅞	11 6	686

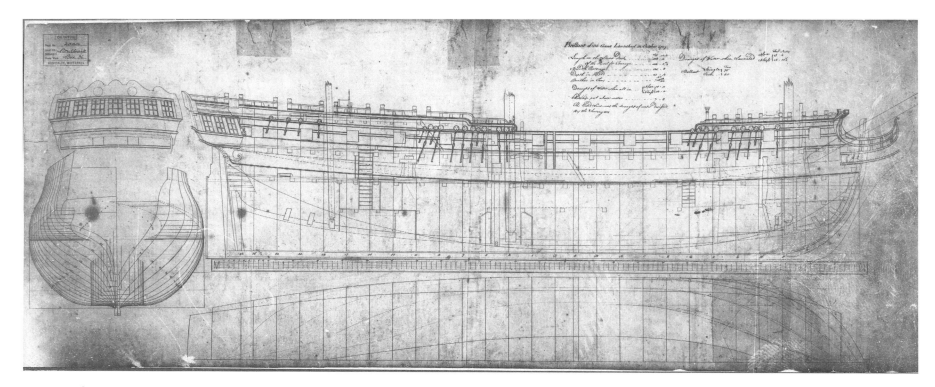

from obsolete designs, it was worth considering in certain circumstances. Of course, the result might not compete for sailing qualities with a purpose-built frigate, and it was both costly and time-consuming to do properly (about 28 months and the cost of a Middling Repair for these two), so it was not widely adopted. However, both these ships proved to be surprisingly good sailers.

Brilliant of 1757, as fitted sheer & profile draught.

Basically enlarged *Southampton*s, the 36s carried four more 6pdrs on the quarterdeck and forecastle. The draughts offer no evidence that they were ever equipped with oarports.

Table 12: RAZÉE 44-GUN SHIPS (32-GUN FIFTH RATES)
Building Data

Name	Builder	Launched	Converted	Conversion ordered	Conversion completed	Fate
Adventure	Blaydes, Hull	1 Oct 1741	Plymouth Dyd	14 Jul 1756	16 Aug 1758	20 Mar 1770 sold
Sapphire	Carter, Limehouse	21 Feb 1741	Deptford Dyd	14 Jul 1756	22 Jun 1758	1780 hulk; 1784 sold

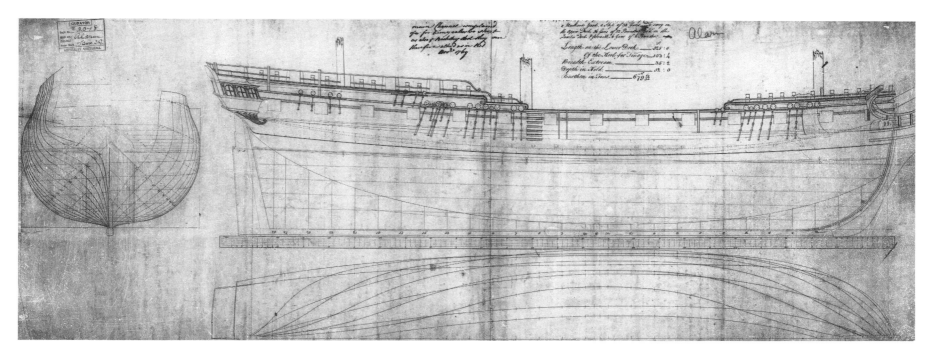

Alarm of 1758, design sheer draught.

The influence of the *Unicorn* class extended beyond the lines, the 1757 group of four *Nigers* having a very similar, rather cramped quarter gallery as seen on the contemporary *Coventry* group. They also introduced the round bow to the larger frigates and upper deck cable-handling, although this early sheer still shows lower deck sweep ports. A note mentions the lengthening of the main channel and the moved backstay stool ordered in November 1769.

4. The Improved Models, 1758-1763

One of Slade's most notable characteristics was his desire for continuous improvement; his many designs for 74-gun ships, for example, underwent a process of constant minor alteration.[19] When the Admiralty ordered three new 32s to be built in September 1757, Slade proposed a separate new design for each:

1. one 'nearly similar to the *Lowestoffe* and *Tartar*' [*ie* to the lines of the *Tygre*];

2. another nearly similar 'to the Amazon' [*ie* the French *Panthère*];

3. and a third similar 'to the *Southampton* with a small alteration'.

This amounts to a carefully planned programme, which would compare the merits of an existing successful hull form (as derived from

the *Tygre*), an extreme example of the French frigate form in the *Amazon*, and a marginally improved current design (the *Southampton*: the ship had been at sea for only two months but it may *cont page 35*

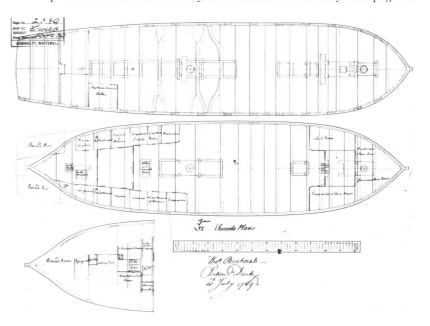

Tweed of 1759, deck plans taken off at Portsmouth 18 July 1769.

The only surviving plans of this intriguing ship do at least give some indication of the relatively long hull; there were fourteen broadside ports, but they were closer together than for other 32s and the foremost port could not realistically admit a gun (the recoil would have damaged the bitts). Upper deck cable handling suggests a round bow. Note that the ship had a magazine aft and storerooms on the lower deck forward, just like the early 28s from which she was derived.

Table 13: *NIGER* CLASS 32-GUN FIFTH RATES
Specification

Armament:	Upper deck	Quarterdeck	Forecastle	Guns	Men
Design	26 x 12pdrs	4 x 6pdrs	2 x 6pdrs	32[1]	210
Added by AO					
11 Nov 1756		12 x ½pdr swivels			
10 Aug 1779		6 x 18pdr carr	2 x 18pdr carr		
25 Dec 1779 [2]		4 x 18pdr carr	2 x 18pdr carr		
19 Nov 1794		4 x 24pdr carr	2 x 24pdr carr		

Designed by Sir Thomas Slade, 'nearly similar to Lowestoffe and Tartar'

	Lower deck	Keel	Breadth	Depth in hold	Burthen
	ft ins	ft ins	ft ins	ft ins	Tons
Design	125 0	103 4	35 2	12 0	679⁶⁷⁄₉₄
As completed					
Niger	125 0	103 4	35 2	12 0	679⁶⁷⁄₉₄
Alarm	125 0	103 4	35 3	12 0	683
Aeolus	125 5½	103 6⅝	35 9	12 0	704
Stag	125 2½	103 8½	35 9½	12 0	706⁶³⁄₉₄
Montreal	125 0⅝	103 4	35 2⅝	12 0	681⁷¹⁄₉₄
Quebec	125 0	103 3	35 4	12 0	685⁶⁰⁄₉₄
Emerald	125 0	103 4½	35 2½	12 0	681³¹⁄₉₄
Pearl	125 0½	103 4⅜	35 3	12 0	683¹⁶⁄₉₄
Winchelsea	125 0	103 4	35 2	12 0	679⁷⁹⁄₉₄
Glory	125 0	103 4	35 2	11 9½	679⁶⁷⁄₉₄
Aurora	125 0	103 3⅜	35 3	12 0	682

Notes:

[1] *Stag* and *Quebec* carried a reduced armament of 22 x 12pdrs, 4 x 6pdrs and 2 x 6pdrs with 200 men and the spars of a 28-gun ship between 1777 (*Quebec* 1778) and 1779.

[2] Actual as opposed to established numbers of carronades, where known, are given in Table 44.

Lowestoffe of 1761, design sheer draught.

Only a body plan with stem and stern profile survive for the *Abenakise* but from this it is clear that *Lowestoffe* has the same plumb stem and relatively upright sternpost. However, the hull form, although following the French two-turn bilge in the midsection, is somewhat less sharp than its prototype, although this did no harm to *Lowestoffe*'s outstanding sailing qualities. A stylistic feature of Slade's later work is the quarter gallery with one large central light flanked by two smaller, a feature already seen in the later *Niger*s and also occurring in the *Mermaid* class.

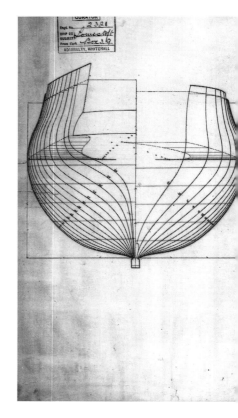

Niger class of 1757, design profile draught.

All the ships of the class are mentioned in the notes on the righthand side. Slade ordered the pumps moved to the upper deck during construction, and from *Emerald* onwards the steeve of the bowsprit was reduced. The alterations to the quarterdeck rails, showing enlarged carronade ports obviously date from a later period (*c*1780). There are alterations dotted in forward, showing the removal of the galley stove from the platform to the lower deck allowing a magazine (the main magazine is aft as in the 28s) and sailroom to be added; this had not been done in *Emerald* in 1763 but is known to have been carried out in 1769 for *Niger* so it is unlikely to have been adopted during construction for any of the ships.

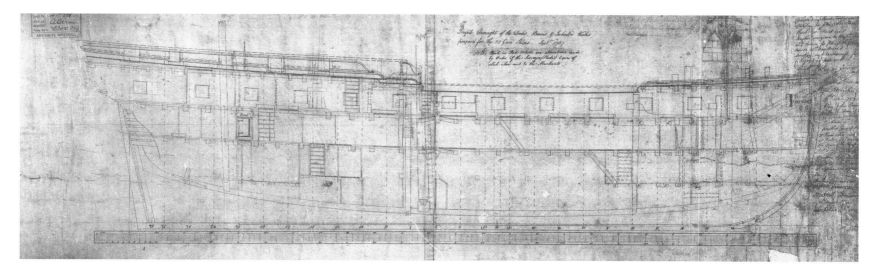

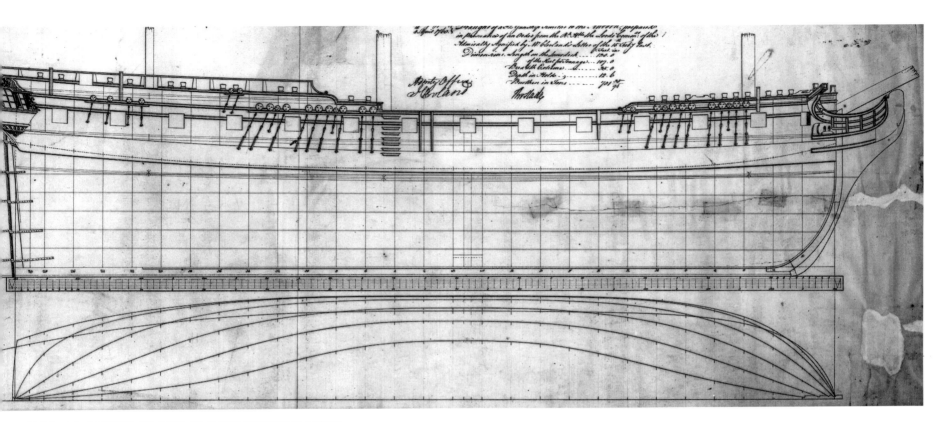

Table 14: *NIGER* CLASS 32-GUN FIFTH RATES
Building Data

Name	Ordered	Builder	Laid Down	Launched	Sailed	Fitted at	Fate
Niger	19 Sep 1757	Sheerness Dyd	7 Feb 1758	25 Sep 1759	?21 Jun 1759	Sheerness	1799 troopship; 1804 28 guns; 1810 prison ship; 1813 renamed *Negro*; 29 Sep 1814 sold
Alarm	19 Sep 1757	Barnard, Harwich	26 Sep 1757	19 Sep 1758[1]	24 Jun 1759	Harwich	Sep 1812 BU at Portsmouth
Aeolus	19 Sep 1757	West, Deptford	Sep 1757	29 Nov 1758	18 Jan 1759	Plymouth	May 1796 hulk at Sheerness; 1800 renamed *Guernsey*; May 1801 BU
Stag	19 Sep 1757	Stanton, Rotherhithe	26 Sep 1757	4 Sep 1758	9 Dec 1758	Deptford	Jul 1783 BU
Montreal	6 Jun 1759	Sheerness Dyd	21 Apr 1760	15 Sep 1761	10 Oct 1761	Sheerness	4 May 1779 captured by the French
Quebec	16 Jul 1759	Barnard, Harwich	Jul 1759	14 Jul 1760	9 Aug 1760	Harwich	6 Oct 1779 blown up in action
Emerald	24 Mar 1759	Blaydes, Hull	13 May 1761	8 Jun 1762	Oct 1762	Hull	1793 BU
Pearl	24 Mar 1759	Chatham Dyd	6 May 1761	27 Mar 1762	14 May 1762	Chatham	Renamed *Prothée* as receiving ship 1825; 4 Jan 1832 sold for BU
Winchelsea	8 Aug 1761	Sheerness Dyd	29 Mar 1762	31 May 1764	21 Nov 1767[2]	Sheerness	1800 troopship; 1803 prison hulk; 3 Nov 1814 sold
Glory	30 Jan 1762	Blaydes & Hodgson, Hull	Mar 1762	24 Oct 1763	Dec 1763	Hull	30 Aug 1774 renamed *Apollo*; Jan 1786 BU
Aurora	30 Apr 1763	Chatham Dyd	10 Oct 1763	13 Jan 1766	Fitted 1769	Chatham	1770 burnt out and foundered at sea

Notes:

[1] AO of 16 Feb 1758 to Barnard to give priority to the *Conqueror*, 74 at the expense of the *Alarm*.

[2] Fitting out did not commence until 26 June 1766 and was completed as above.

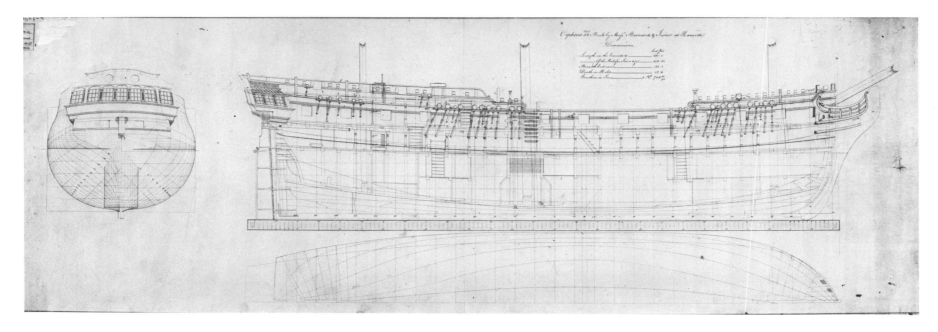

Orpheus of 1773, as fitted sheer & profile draught.

Although treated in all official refernces as a sister of *Lowestoffe*, this ship and the *Diamond* exhibit slight changes to the lines, resulting in a more rounded midship section. It was Slade's habit to continually modify his designs so this is not unusual; but neither of the later ships was as good under sail as *Lowestoffe*.

Table 15: *TWEED* CLASS 32-GUN FIFTH RATE
Specification

Armament:	Upper deck	Quarterdeck	Forecastle	Guns	Men
Design	26 x 12pdrs	4 x 6pdrs	2 x 6pdrs	32	210
		12 x ½pdr swivels			

Designed by Sir Thomas Slade, 'similar to the Tartar lengthened'

	Lower deck	Keel	Breadth	Depth in hold	Burthen
	ft ins	ft ins	ft ins	ft ins	Tons
Design	128 3	107 8	33 10	10 4	655⁴⁹⁄₉₄
As completed					
Tweed	128 4½	107 9	33 11½	10 4	660⁸⁶⁄₉₄

Table 16: *TWEED* CLASS 32-GUN FIFTH RATE
Building Data

Name	Ordered	Builder	Laid Down	Launched	Sailed	Fitted at	Fate
Tweed	26 Nov 1757	Blaydes, Hull	19 Jan 1758	28 Apr 1759	21 Jun 1759	Hull	1776 sold

Table 17: *LOWESTOFFE* CLASS 32-GUN FIFTH RATES
Specification

Armament:	Upper deck	Quarterdeck	Forecastle	Guns	Men
Design	26 x 12pdrs	4 x 6pdrs	2 x 6pdrs	32	220
		12 x ½pdr swivels			
Added by AO					
10 Aug 1779		6 x 18pdr carr	2 x 18pdr carr		
25 Dec 1779[1]		4 x 18pdr carr	2 x 18pdr carr		
19 Nov 1794		4 x 24pdr carr	2 x 24pdr carr		

Designed by Sir Thomas Slade, 'nearly similar to the Aurora prize'

	Lower deck	Keel	Breadth	Depth in hold	Burthen
	ft ins	ft ins	ft ins	ft ins	tons
LEAD SHIP					
Design	130 0	107 0	35 0	12 6	701³⁵⁄₉₄
As completed					
Lowestoffe	130 6	107 1½	35 3¾	12 6	717¹⁶⁄₉₄
SECOND GROUP					
Design	130 0	108 2½	35 0	12 6	705
As completed					
Orpheus	130 6	105 5	35 1	12 6	710
Diamond	130 0	108 2½	35 1	12 6	708⁴⁰⁄₉₄

Notes:

[1] Actual as opposed to established numbers of carronades, where known, are given in Table 44.

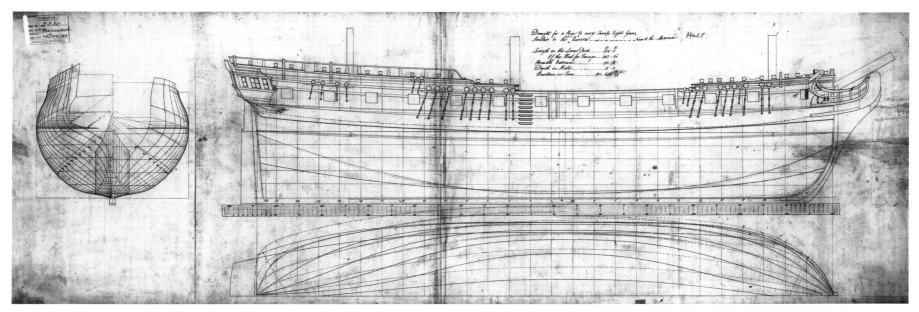

Mermaid of 1761, design sheer draught.

Although similarly based on the principles of the *Abenakise* hull form, the *Mermaid* class departed further than the *Lowestoffe* from exact copying of the midsection; but the results were less impressive. The class shared stylistic features with the simultaneously designed 32, including the quarter gallery and square French-style hances.

have been long enough to discover that she was only a moderate sailer). A similar comparative approach was already employed for sloops,[20] but frigates may well have been too important too risk in this way, and after discussions only the first design was adopted.

The ensuing ships became known as the *Niger* or *Alarm* class, which was an outstanding success; more ships were built to this design than any other 32 of the Seven Years War. They were fast, weatherly, robust and seaworthy, carrying their guns over 7ft from the waterline when fully stored. They were armed like their slightly smaller predecessors, but the improvements included the round bow and cable handling on the upper deck, leaving the lower deck free for the better accommodation of the crew.

The success of the *Niger*s robbed Slade of the opportunity to improve the *Southampton*, but in a way it helped him achieve his other desire, to test the long, low and lightly constructed French design style. A couple of months after his *Amazon* proposal was turned down, he was able to persuade the Admiralty to build an experimental 32 to the lines of the *Tygre* but incorporating an extra 10ft section amidships. Launched as the *Tweed*, the ship provided a salutary lesson in the advantages and disadvantages of the French approach: the ship was very fast, having managed 13kts when six months foul, and regularly outsailed both *Niger* class 32s and *Unicorn* class 28s (considered the benchmark for frigate performance); against this, the ship was tender, shipped a lot of water, carried her guns 1ft nearer the waterline than other 32s, and strained her upperworks, 'being slight built'.[21] The experiment was not repeated and in 1776, at a time of national crisis when every available frigate was being refitted for service, it was decided to sell the *Tweed* because the state of hull made her uneconomic to repair.

During the course of the Seven Years War a large number of French national and privateer frigates were captured, the vast majority of which were carefully surveyed and reports forwarded to the Admiralty. There was no longer a desperate need for radical improvements in cruiser

Table 18: *LOWESTOFFE* CLASS 32-GUN FIFTH RATES
Building Data

Name	Ordered	Builder	Laid Down	Launched	Sailed	Fitted at	Fate
LEAD SHIP							
Lowestoffe	24 Apr 1760	West, Deptford	9 May 1760	5 Jun 1761	1 Aug 1761	Deptford	11 Aug 1811 wrecked in West Indies
SECOND GROUP							
Orpheus	25 Dec 1770	Barnard, Harwich	May 1771	7 May 1773	24 May 1773	Harwich	15 Aug 1778 burnt to avoid capture
Diamond	25 Dec 1770	Blaydes & Hodges, Hull	May 1771	28 May 1774	13 Jun 1774	Hull	30 Dec 1784 sold

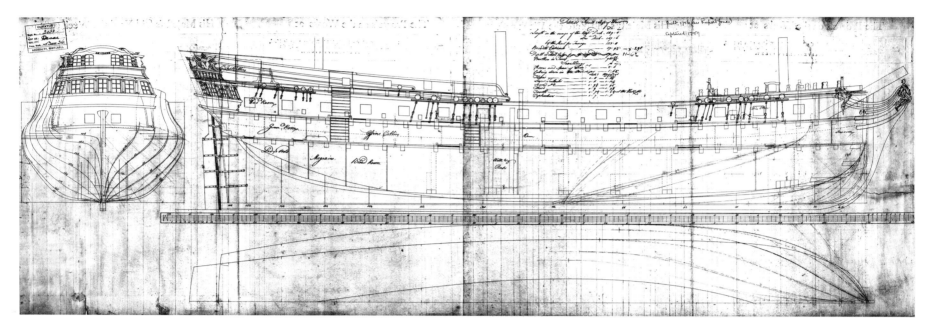

Table 19: *MERMAID* CLASS 28-GUN SIXTH RATES
Specification

Armament:	Upper deck	Quarterdeck	Forecastle	Guns	Men
	24 x 9pdrs	4 x 3pdrs		28	200
		12 x ½pdr swivels			

Added by AO

| **10 Aug 1779** [1] | | 4 x 18pdr carr | 2 x 18pdr carr | | |
| **2 Feb 1780** | | 6pdrs in lieu of 3pdrs | | | |

Designed by Sir Thomas Slade 'nearly similar to Aurora Prize'

	Lower deck	Keel	Breadth	Depth in hold	Burthen
	ft ins	ft ins	ft ins	ft ins	tons
FIRST GROUP					
Design	124 0	102 8⅛	33 6	11 0	612 72/94
As completed					
Mermaid	124 0	102 8¼	33 6⅜	11 0	613 85/94
Hussar	124 4	103 8½	33 10⅜	11 0	627 64/94
Solebay	124 0	102 8½	33 8	11 0	619 4/94
SECOND GROUP					
Design	124 0	103 4¾	33 6	11 0	617 22/94
As completed					
Greyhound	124 2	102 8⅞	33 7½	11 0	618
Triton	124 1	103 4⅝	33 7	11 0	620
Boreas	124 6	103 11	33 8	10 11½	626

Notes:
[1] The actual as opposed to established carronades, where known, are given in Table 44.

Danae, ex-French, as captured sheer & profile draught 1759.

Most of the opposing frigates during the Seven Years War were 8pdr-armed, which were easily outmatched by British 12pdr ships, even though some French cruisers were very large indeed. With the exception of the half-battery *Abenakise*, the largest captured frigate was the 941-ton *Danae*. Like many French frigates of her day, she has a small cabin on the quarterdeck.

design, but one prize, the huge 950-ton *L'Abenakise*,[22] particularly appealed to Slade's enquiring mind. Having seen the ship and 'approving very much of the form of her body', he advocated adopting the ship as model for the next class of frigates. The ship was certainly a fast sailer, but in layout was a throwback to the *demi-batterie* ship of the first half of the century, carrying eight 18pdrs on the lower deck, and a full battery of twenty-eight 12pdrs above, plus quarterdeck 6pdrs. These rather awkward proportions were to give Slade some difficulty when his lobbying for the design proved all too successful.

In February 1760 the Admiralty ordered draughts for a 74, a 64, a 32, a 28 and a sloop based on the lines of this ship, now called the *Aurora* in British service. The Navy Board was forced to point out how difficult it was to follow this instruction to the letter (see Chapter 12), and the new designs were described as 'nearly similar to the Aurora', being close derivatives but not merely scaled up or down from the original lines. A single 32 and 28, the *Lowestoffe* and *Mermaid* respectively, were ordered on 24 April 1760 to the new designs, both being somewhat larger than previous ships of their class, but nowhere near the size of some of their French equivalents.[23] *Lowestoffe* was a very fine sailer (14kts were reported on one occasion), but although surviving records suggest that *Mermaid* was less successful, two further slightly modified class members were added in 1762.

As usual in peacetime, after 1763 cruiser design work was confined to a couple of sloops, but when a breach with Spain over the Falkland

Table 20: *MERMAID* CLASS 28-GUN SIXTH RATES
Building Data

Name	Ordered	Builder	Laid Down	Launched	Sailed	Fitted at	Fate
FIRST GROUP							
Mermaid	24 Apr 1760	Blaydes, Hull	27 May 1760	6 May 1761	Sep 1761	Hull	8 Aug 1778 run ashore to avoid capture
Hussar	30 Jan 1762	Inwood, Rotherhithe	1 Apr 1762	26 Aug 1763	7 Nov 1763	Deptford	Nov 1779 wrecked off New York
Solebay	30 Jan 1762	Airey, Newcastle	10 May 1762	9 Sep 1763	Dec 1763	Newcastle	25 Jan 1782 wrecked Nevis, West Indies
SECOND GROUP							
Greyhound	25 Dec 1770	Adams, Bucklers Hard	Feb 1771	20 Jul 1773	29 Jul 1773		1781 wrecked off Deal
Triton	25 Dec 1770	Adams, Bucklers Hard	Feb 1771	1 Oct 1773	14 Oct 1773		Jan 1796 BU
Boreas	25 Dec 1770	Blaydes & Hodgson, Hull	May 1771	23 Aug 1774	8 Sep 1774		1797 slop ship; May 1802 sold

Islands threatened war in 1770 both the *Lowestoffe* and *Mermaid* classes were revived, alongside new but more conventional designs by John Williams, the new Surveyor. Thomas Slade died in February 1771, and the most productive era of eighteenth century British ship design came to an end. Paying tribute to this talented but under-appreciated naval architect, Sir John Henslow, himself a Surveyor in the 1790s, wrote: 'My late very esteemed friend and patron, Sir Thomas Slade, he was truly a great man in the line he took, such a one I believe never went before him, and if I am not too partial, I may venture to say will hardly follow him.' This reverence for the work of an earlier master was to set the tone for the following generation.

Enterprize **class of 1770, design sheer draught.**
Although they resembled the earlier *Unicorn*s very closely in layout and armament, they were significantly poorer performers under sail. This draught shows in dotted line the solid quarterdeck bulwark and raised waist introduced during the American Revolutionary War.

5. *The Second Generation, 1773-1785*

The Falkland Islands affair sparked a small programme of frigate building that eventually produced eight 28s and five 32s, launched in leisurely fashion between 1773 and 1775, long after the crisis was resolved. However, it gave John Williams, the relatively new Surveyor, his first opportunity to try his hand at frigate design. To be built in parallel with Slade's *Aurora*-derived *Mermaid* (28) and *Lowestoffe* (32) classes were Williams's equivalents, the *Enterprize* and *Amazon* respectively. Both harked back in specification, proportions and basic hull form to previous models, and in a general way resembled the *Unicorn*s and *Niger*s. However, the sailing qualities of the new ships were not as outstanding as those of their predecessors. Of course Williams may have felt inhibited by working alongside the great man,

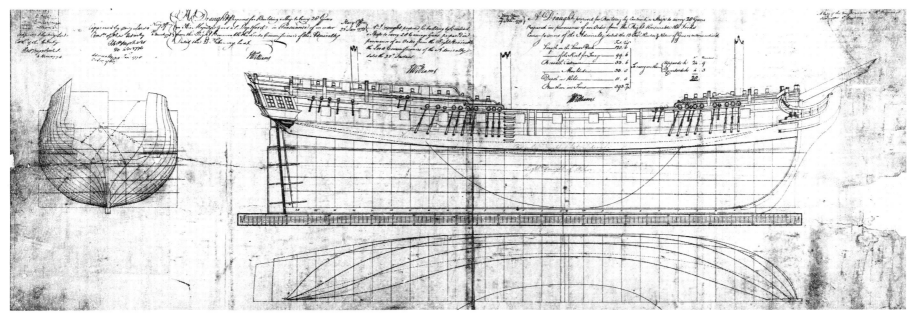

Table 21: CAPTURED SHIPS 1756-1763

| Name, rate | Nationality | Built | Captured | Dimensions | | | | | | | Armament | | | | Fate |
| | | | | Lower deck | | Keel | | Breadth | | Depth in hold | | Burthen | Gundeck | Upper deck | Quarter-deck | Fore-castle | |
				ft	ins	ft	ins	ft	ins	ft	ins	tons	(No x cal)	(No x cal)	(No x cal)	(No x cal)	
Equivalents of English 28s																	
Emerald, 28 ex-*Emeraude*, 26	Fr	1741	25 Oct 1757	115	4	93	1⅝	33	11½	9	3¾	571		24 x 9 24 x 8	4 x 4 2 x 6[1]		Nov 1761 BU
Vengeance, 28	Fr privateer	St Malo, 1757	Feb 1758	116	11	95	10¾	32	4	11	3½	533		24 x 9	4 x 4		Oct 1766 sunk as breakwater
Valeur, 28	Fr	Rochefort, 1753	18 Oct 1759	115	6	93	4	32	6	10	10	524		18 x 9, 6 x 6	4 x 3		26 Jan 1764 sold
Equivalents of English 32s																	
Crescent, 32 ex-*Rostan*	Fr privateer	?	Feb 1758	130	5	107	6½	35	9	11	2	731		24 x 12	6 x 6	2 x 6	13 Jun 1777 sold
Repulse, 32 ex-*Bellone*, 32	Fr	Rochefort, 1755	21 Feb 1759	122	7	104	1	34	11½	10	10½	676^{56}/₉₄		26 x 12 28 x 8	4 x 6 4 x 4	2 x 6	Dec 1776 foundered
Arethusa, 32 ex-*Arethuse*	Fr	Purchased 1758	18 May 1759	132	1	110	10⅜	34	5½	10	8	700^{19}/₉₄		26 x 12	4 x 6	2 x 6	19 Mar 1779 wrecked
Blonde, 32 ex-*Embuscade*, 40	Fr	Le Havre, 1755	28 Apr 1760	133	0	109	0¼	34	10	10	7	703^{57}/₉₄		26 x 12 26 x 8	4 x 6 4 x 4	2 x 6 2 x 6	21 Jan 1782 wrecked
Flora, 32 ex-*Vestale*	Fr	Nantes, 1756	8 Jan 1761	131	7	110	1¼	34	6½	10	9	698^{67}/₉₄		26 x 12	4 x 6	2 x 6	7 Aug 1778 scuttled
Brune, 32	Fr	Le Havre, 1755	30 Jan 1761	131	2	108	11¾	34	7½	10	8	694^{86}/₉₄		26 x 12	4 x 6	2 x 6	2 Oct 1792 sold
Boulogne, 32 ex-*Boullonge*	Fr East India Co ship	Lorient, 1758	Mar 1761	133	8	111	10⅝	33	3	13	4	657^{71}/₉₄		26 x 12	4 x 6	2 x 6	Jul 1784 hulked
Baleine, 32 ex-20	Fr flûte	1758	Oct 1760	149	10⅞	129	0¾	32	0	12	9	702½		26 x 12[3]	4 x 6	2 x 6	23 Jun 1767 sold
Larger than English 32s																	
Aurora, 38 ex-*L'Abenakise*, 38	Fr	Quebec, 1756	23 Nov 1757	144	0	118	9	38	8½	15	2	946	8 x 18[2] 8 x 18	28 x 12 28 x 12		2 x 6 2 x 6	Apr 1763 BU
Melampe, 36	Fr privateer	Bayonne, 1757	2 Nov 1757	134	6	111	6½	35	6	11	3½	747^{66}/₉₄		26 x 12	8 x 6	2 x 6	1764 laid up, Antigua
Danae, 38	Fr	Le Havre, 1756	28 Mar 1759	147	6	123	11	37	9½	11	4½	941		30 x 12	6 x 6	2 x 6	14 Jun 1771 BU comp

Notes:

The table includes only those ships taken into British service. In many cases detailed surveys exist for other ships, including the privateers *Victoire* (425 tons) and *Cherzine* (484 tons), and the French national frigates *Hermione* (812 tons) and *Comète* (647 tons). The first armament listed is as fitted for British service; the second is as captured, where known.

[1] The disposition of guns is uncertain.

[2] Later reduced to 24 x 12 on upper deck, 4 x 6 on quarter deck, 2 x 6 on forecastle.

[3] Rated 20-gun Sixth Rate by end of war, but armament unknown.

but when frigate building began again a few years later, Williams did not feel the need to revise his existing designs. On Slade's death, Williams was joined by a more innovative co-Surveyor, Edward Hunt, but Williams himself was convinced that no radical improvements were necessary, an opinion he even expressed to the King: 'The dimensions of the present ships of the Royal Navy have been found by experience to be proper and sufficiently great for the weight of metal they are to carry, the proportions of the length to the breadth; also the depth in hold proper to both.'[24]

At this time there were signs of a growing shortage of native British oak, and the Navy Board proposed using some of the frigates of the Falklands emergency programme to test the durability of foreign oak. They were to be built in the Dockyards so that the Board would be certain of the quality of construction in order to allow a fair comparison. Initially two 28s, *Surprize* and *Enterprize*, were chosen to carry out this experiment, but a third, *Actaeon*, was added to test timber 'that had undergone Mr Jackson's process' of seasoning. The results must have been confusing: *Surprize* was sold after a mere nine years' service, whereas *Enterprize* was not broken up until 1807; *Actaeon* was burnt to avoid capture in her first commission.

The Admiralty's response to the growing unrest in Britain's North American colonies is instructive. The first new construction that might indicate a departure from a peacetime norm was the ordering of three sloops in 1775, but in 1776 a new class of 9pdr armed 20-gun (later 24-gun) ships was designed and the construction of 28s recommenced with two additions to Williams's *Enterprize* class. Over the next three years a further fifteen 28s were built, but the most significant development was the revival of the two-decked 44-gun ship in preference to the 12pdr frigate. Only two experimental prototype 44s had been built since the abandonment of the Establishment, and it is clear that the new vessels were a specific reaction to the peculiar circumstances of colonial warfare.

The Americans decided to build a limited frigate force of thirteen ships at the end of 1775[25], but the Admiralty persisted with its mixed force of small frigates and sloops combined with a stiffening of 50-gun ships initially and then the new 44s. At this stage, the conflict was largely one of blockade, amphibious assaults and coastal raids, and the naval opposition consisted entirely of relatively small converted merchantmen and privateers. The small frigates were ideal to counter the latter, while America's highly indented coastline required shallow draught if any of the above tactics were to succeed. In these circumstances, the 44 seems to have been conceived as an economical substitute for a battleship, acting not only as a flagship for the small squadrons then employed but also as the local 'ship of force', likely to be more powerful than anything the colonists' makeshift navy could deploy. They drew relatively little water, so might be used for shore bombardment, and were cheap enough to risk where grounding was a real possibility. In these respects the 44 was superior to the 50, while the advantage of the latter's 24pdr guns would be minimal against the kind of 'soft' targets envisaged.

This may seem like a digression from the frigate story, but it serves

Table 22: *ENTERPRIZE* CLASS 28-GUN SIXTH RATES
Specification

Armament:	Upper deck	Quarterdeck	Forecastle	Guns	Men
Design	24 x 9pdrs	4 x 3pdrs		28	200
		12 x ½pdr swivels			
Added by AO:					
10 Aug 1779[1]		4 x 18pdr carr	2 x 18pdr carr		
2 Feb 1780		6pdrs in lieu of 3pdrs			

Designed by Sir John Williams

	Lower deck	Keel	Breadth	Depth in hold	Burthen
	ft ins	ft ins	ft ins	ft ins	tons
Design	120 6	99 6	33 6	11 0	593 89/94
As completed					
Siren	120 10	99 7½	33 9	10 9	603 40/94
Fox	120 6	99 6	33 8	11 0	600
Surprize	120 6	99 6	33 6	11 0	594
Enterprize	120 6	99 6	33 6	11 0	594
Actaeon	120 6½	99 6	33 6	11 0¼	594
Medea	120 9½	99 4	33 10	11 0½	605
Proserpine	120 6	99 9	33 7½	11 0	595
Andromeda	120 9	99 7⅝	33 8	11 0	601
Aurora	120 6	99 4	33 7	11 0	596
Sibyl	120 7	99 7⅝	33 7½	11 0	599
Brilliant	120 6¼	99 6	33 8	11 0	600
Pomona	120 6	99 6	33 6	11 0	594
Crescent	120 8	99 5	34 0	11 0	611
Nemesis	120 7	99 6	33 7½	11 0	598
Resource	120 8	99 7	33 9	11 0½	603
Mercury	120 9¾	99 10½	33 9	11 0½	605
Pegasus	120 6	99 6	33 6	11 0	594
Cyclops	120 6	99 6	33 9	11 0	603
Vestal	120 6	99 6	33 8½	11 0½	601
Laurel	120 8¼	99 6¾	33 8½	11 0	602
Hussar	120 6	99 0	33 8	11 0	596 79/94
Rose	120 5½	99 5	33 7¾	11 0	598 55/94
Dido	120 5	99 3	33 7	11 0	595
Thisbe	120 6	99 5⅜	33 7	11 0	596
Circe	120 6⅜	99 5	33 7¾	11 0	599
Alligator	120 6	99 5	33 7½	11 0	599 42/94
Lapwing	120 6	99 4½	33 8	11 0½	597 82/94

Notes:
[1] The actual as opposed to established numbers of carronades, where known, are given in Table 44.

Table 23: *ENTERPRIZE* CLASS 28-GUN SIXTH RATES
Building Data

Name	Ordered	Builder	Laid Down	Launched	Sailed	Fitted at	Fate
Siren	25 Dec 1770	Henniker, Rochester	Apr 1771	2 Nov 1773	5 Oct 1775	Chatham	10 Nov 1777 wrecked off Rhode Island
Fox	25 Dec 1770	Calhoun, Northam	May 1771	2 Sep 1773	12 Feb 1776	Portsmouth	17 Sep 1778 taken by French *Junon*
Surprize	Jan 1771	Woolwich Dyd	5 Sep 1771	13 Apr 1774	15 Apr 1775	Woolwich	17 Apr 1783 sold
Enterprize	Jan 1771	Deptford Dyd	9 Sep 1771	24 Aug 1774	20 Jun 1775	Deptford	1799 hulked; Aug 1807 sold
Actaeon	5 Nov 1771	Woolwich Dyd	Oct 1772	18 Apr 1775	3 Aug 1775	Woolwich	29 Jun 1776 burnt to avoid capture
Medea	14 May 1776	Hilhouse, Bristol	June 1776	28 Apr 1778	15 Sep 1778	Plymouth	1795 sold
Proserpine	14 May 1776	Barnard, Harwich	Jun 1776	7 Jul 1777	23 Sep 1777	Sheerness	1 Feb 1799 wrecked near Cuxhaven
Andromeda	24 May 1776	Fabian, East Cowes	Jul 1776	18 Nov 1777	28 Jan 1778	Portsmouth	Dec 1780 lost in hurricane, Martinique
Aurora	3 Jul 1776	Perry, Blackwall	Jul 1776	7 Jun 1777	24 Jun 1777	?Deptford	3 Nov 1814 sold
Sibyl	24 Jul 1776	Adams, Bucklers Hard	10 Dec 1776	2 Jan 1779	13 Mar 1779	Portsmouth	14 Jul 1795 renamed *Garland*; 26 Jul 1798 wrecked off Madagascar
Brilliant	9 Oct 1776	Adams, Bucklers Hard	Feb 1777	15 Jul 1779	4 Sep 1779	Portsmouth	Nov 1811 BU at Portsmouth
Pomona	7 Mar 1777[1]	Raymond, Northam	May 1777	22 Sep 1778	17 Dec 1778	Portsmouth	14 Jul 1795 renamed *Amphitrite*; Aug 1811 BU
Crescent	19 Jul 1777	Hilhouse, Bristol	19 Aug 1777	Mar 1779	May 1779	Bristol	19 Jun 1781 taken by French off Cadiz
Nemesis	30 Sep 1777	Jolly & Smallshaw, Liverpool	Nov 1777	23 Jan 1780	4 Jun 1780	Liverpool	1812 troopship; 9 Jun 1814 sold
Resource	30 Sep 1777	Randall, Rotherhithe	Nov 1777	10 Aug 1778	2 Oct 1778	Deptford	1800 troopship; 1804 floating battery; 1806 renamed *Enterprize*; 28 Aug 1816 sold
Mercury	22 Jan 1778	Mestears, Thames	25 Mar 1778	9 Dec 1779	24 Feb 1780	Deptford	1803 floating battery; 1810 troopship; Jan 1814 BU at Woolwich
Pegasus	21 Feb 1778	Deptford Dyd	20 Jun 1778	1 Jun 1779	20 Jul 1779	Deptford	1814 hulk; 28 Aug 1816 sold
Cyclops	6 Mar 1778	Batson, Limehouse	3 Apr 1778	31 Jul 1779	26 Sep 1779	Deptford	Mar 1800 troopship; 1 Sep 1814 sold
Vestal	18 Mar 1778	Batson, Limehouse	1 May 1778	24 Dec 1779	25 Feb 1780	Deptford	1800 troopship; Feb 1816 sold, Barbados
Laurel	30 Apr 1778	Raymond, Northam	3 Jun 1778	27 Oct 1779	31 Oct 1779	Portsmouth	10 Oct 1780 lost in hurricane, W Indies
Hussar		Wilson, Sandgate	Jun 1782	1 Sep 1784	To Ordinary	Deptford	27 Dec 1797 wrecked off Ile Bas
Rose		Stewart & Hall, Sandgate	Jun 1782	1 Jul 1783	23 Oct 1783	Deptford	28 Jun 1794 wrecked off Jamaica
Dido		Stewart & Hall, Sandgate	Sep 1782	27 Nov 1784	To Ordinary	Deptford	1800 troopship; 3 Apr 1817 sold
Thisbe		King, Dover	Sep 1782	25 Nov 1783	17 Apr 1784	Deptford	1800 troopship; 9 Aug 1815 sold
Circe		Ladd, Dover	Dec 1782	30 Sep 1785	5 Nov 1785	Deptford	16 Nov 1803 wrecked off Yarmouth
Alligator		Jacobs, Sandgate	Dec 1782	18 Apr 1787	To Ordinary	Deptford	1810 hulk; 21 Jul 1814 sold
Lapwing		King, Dover	Feb 1783	21 Sep 1785	To Ordinary	Deptford	1813 hulk; May 1828 BU

Notes:
[1] Contract date.

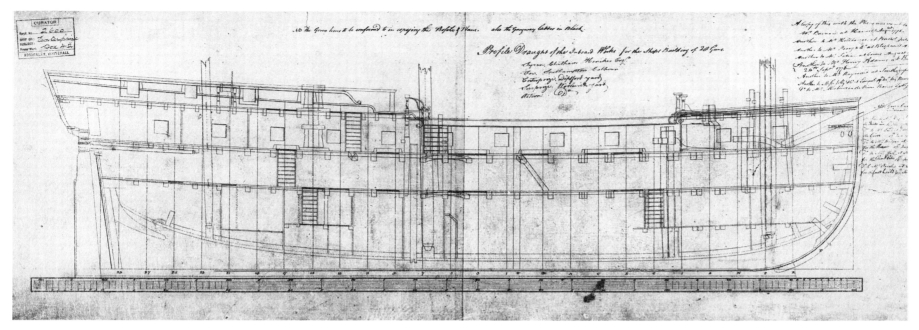

Enterprize class of 1770, design profile draught.

This draught mentions all the ships of the class; those ordered in 1782 (*Hussar* and later) had the solid quarterdeck bulwarks and raised waist as built.

Circe of 1785, as fitted sheer & profile.

The final appearance of the class with solid quarterdeck barricades and raised waist. Note the reintroduction of sweep ports, between the guns, which were omitted from the earlier draughts; in general they were not fitted in peacetime, but were usually found useful in war. The beautifully detailed as fitted draughts of the 1770s gradually became less elaborate under the pressure of war, but this example gives some idea of external mouldings and the decoration to quarter gallery and cathead.

to underline the essentially fleet and high seas cruising role of the bigger frigate. None was built in response either to the American frigate programme of 1776, or to the upsurge of commerce raiding in 1777;[26] significantly, the other type not ordered in this period was the 74, the line of battle ship *par excellence*, but both were promptly reintroduced into the building programme – and in numbers – as soon as France entered the arena in 1778. Eight 32s were ordered in the course of the year, three to the existing *Amazon* draught, but true to the now well established principle of comparative designs, the younger Surveyor, Edward Hunt, produced a new draught for the other five vessels. These

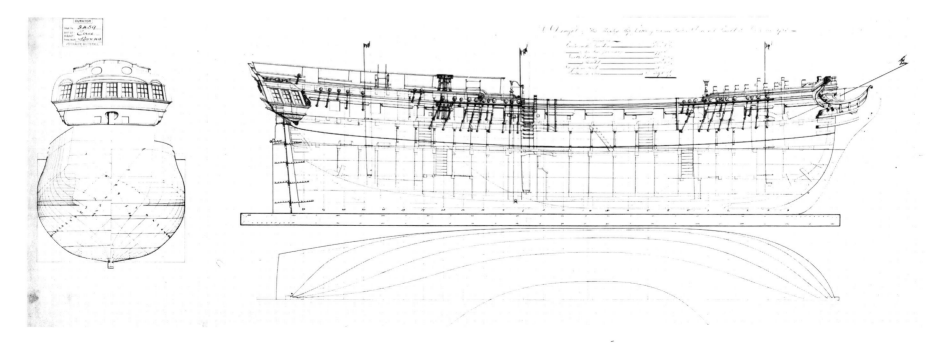

Table 24: *AMAZON* CLASS 32-GUN FIFTH RATES
Specification

Armament:	Upper deck	Quarterdeck	Forecastle	Guns	Men
Design	26 x 12pdrs	4 x 6pdrs	2 x 6pdrs	32	210
		12 x ½pdr swivels			
Added by AO					
10 Aug 1779		6 x 18pdr carr	2 x 18pdr carr		
25 Dec 1779[1]		4 x 18pdr carr	2 x 18pdr carr		
19 Nov 1794		4 x 24pdr carr	2 x 24pdr carr		

Designed by Sir John Williams

	Lower deck	Keel	Breadth	Depth in hold	Burthen
	ft ins	ft ins	ft ins	ft ins	tons
Design	126 0	104 0	35 0	12 2	677 62/94
As completed					
Amazon	126 0	104 0	35 2	12 2½	687
Thetis	126 1	?	35 2	?	686
Ambuscade [F]	126 3	104 1	35 1¾	12 2	684
Cleopatra	126 5	104 6¼	35 2½	12 1¼	689
Amphion	126 1	104 3	35 0	12 2	679
Orpheus	126 4	104 5⅜	35 2½	12 2	688
Juno	126 6½	104 7½	35 2¼	12 1½	689 29/94
Success	126 0	103 10⅜	35 2	12 2	683 20/94
Iphigenia	126 2	104 3	35 0½	12 2	680 72/94
Andromache	126 2	104 0	35 2	12 2	683
Syren	126 0	103 10	35 1¾	12 2	679 8/94
Iris	126 2½	104 3⅛	35 3½	12 2½	687 90/94
Greyhound	126 0	103 11⅝	35 1½	12 2	682
Terpsichore	126 0	103 11⅝	35 1½	12 2	682 4/94
Meleager	126 0	104 0	35 1½	12 2½	682
Castor	126 0	104 0	35 1	12 2	680 77/94
Solebay	126 3½	104 5½	35 0¾	12 2½	683
Blonde	126 6	104 2⅜	35 1	12 2	682

Notes:

[F] Fir-built

[1] Actual as opposed to established numbers of carronades, where known, are given in Table 44.

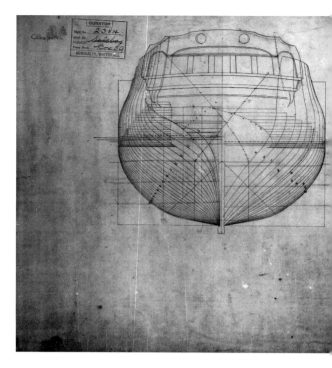

Amazon class of 1770, design sheer draught.

This class followed the pattern of the *Niger*s (indeed, the draught mentions Slade's *Winchelsea*) as the 28s followed the *Unicorn*s, and with the same degradation in performance. The draught notes the design load draught as 16ft 0in forward and 17ft 0in aft which would probably have been exceed when victualled for 6 months.

came to be known as the *Active* class, and seem to have been a disappointment both to their projector and to the Navy at large.

Although Hunt had tried to vary the formula a little, giving the ships slightly less hollow in the garboards and a touch more deadrise, it is worth remembering that the basic specification for all these ships had remained essentially unchanged for over twenty years, since the very introduction of the 32-gun frigate. No doubt this reflected the general satisfaction with the *Niger* class – and possibly a veneration for Slade's achievements – but it made no sense to restrict the Surveyor merely to tinkering with a successful design; the Navy would have been better off continuing to build *Niger*s, and setting the Surveyors to work on genuinely new types.

The true source of design conservatism at this time is not at all clear, because both the Admiralty and the Navy Board were quick to perceive the need for a more powerful type of frigate. France had given up the construction of 8pdr armed frigates in 1774, and while most French 12pdr ships carried twenty-six in the main battery, there had been a few with twenty-eight or even thirty, and more of these larger ships were in prospect.[27] On 21 October 1778 the Admiralty instructed the Navy Board to propose no more frigates of less than 32 guns and to consider 36- and 38-gun ships capable of bearing twenty-eight 12pdrs on the upper deck and 6pdrs on the quarterdeck. The Navy Board's

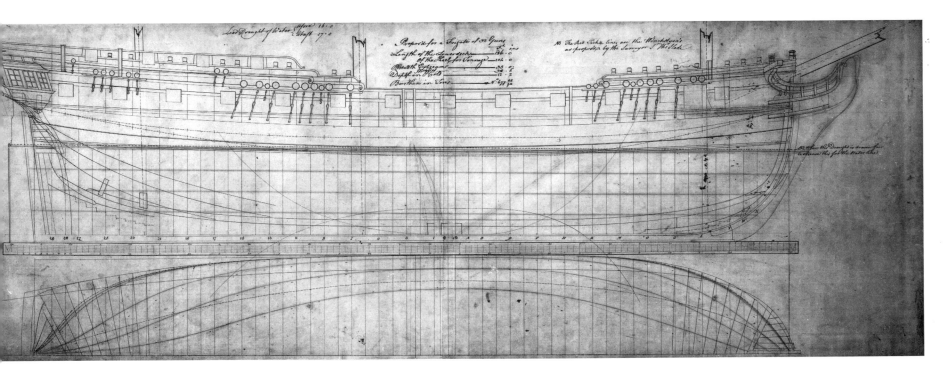

Table 25: *AMAZON* CLASS 32-GUN FIFTH RATES
Building Data

Name	Ordered	Builder	Laid Down	Launched	Sailed	Fitted at	Fate
Amazon	25 Dec 1770	Wells, Rotherhithe	Apr 1771	24 May 1773	19 Jul 1773	Deptford	Jun 1794 BU at Plymouth
Thetis	25 Dec 1770	Adams, Bucklers Hard	Feb 1771	2 Nov 1773	13 Nov 1773	?Portsmouth	12 May 1781 wrecked off St Lucia
Ambuscade [F]	cFeb 1771	Adams, Deptford	Apr 1771	17 Sep 1773	1 Oct 1773	Deptford	Aug 1810 BU (in French hands 1798-1803)
Cleopatra	13 May 1778	Hilhouse, Bristol	6 Jul 1778	26 Nov 1779	9 Jul 1780	Bristol	Sep 1814 BU (in French hands for a week in Feb 1805)
Amphion	11 Jun 1778	Chatham Dyd	1 Oct 1778	27 Dec 1780	9 Feb 1781	Chatham	22 Sep 1796 blown up in an accident
Orpheus	2 Oct 1778	Adams & Barnard, Deptford	7 Jul 1779	3 Jun 1780	15 Jul 1780	Deptford	23 Jan 1807 wrecked in West Indies
Juno	21 Oct 1778	Batson, Limehouse	Dec 1778	30 Sep 1780	14 Dec 1780	Deptford	Jul 1811 BU
Success	22 Feb 1779	Sutton, Liverpool	8 May 1779	10 Apr 1781	Jul 1781	?Liverpool	Jan 1814 convict ship; 1820 BU
Iphigenia	26 Feb 1779	Betts, Mistleythorn	25 May 1779	27 Dec 1780	11 May 1781	Chatham[1]	20 Jul 1801 burnt out in an accident
Andromache	1 Feb 1780	Barnard, Deptford	Jun 1780	17 Nov 1781	4 Jan 1782	Deptford	Sep 1811 BU
Syren	1781	Betts, Mistleythorn	Feb 1781	24 Sep 1782	16 Dec 1782	Chatham[1]	1805 hulked; Sep 1822 BU
Iris	1781	Barnard, Deptford	Jan 1782	2 May 1783	28 Aug 1783	Deptford[2]	Oct 1803 to Trinity House; 1808 renamed *Solebay*; Oct 1833 BU at Devonport
Greyhound	1781	Betts, Mistleythorn	Jan 1782	11 Dec 1783	21 Jan 1784	Chatham	4 Oct 1808 wrecked in the Philippines
Terpsichore	1782	Betts, Mistleythorn	Nov 1782	17 Dec 1785	31 Jan 1786	Chatham	1818 receiving ship; Nov 1830 BU
Meleager	1782	Graves, Frindsbury	Dec 1782	28 Feb 1785	25 Apr 1785	Chatham[2]	9 Jun 1801 wrecked in Gulf of Mexico
Castor	1782	Graham, Harwich	Jan 1783	26 May 1785	11 Jul 1786	Chatham[2]	22 Jul 1819 sold (in French hands for 3 weeks in May 1794)
Solebay	1783	Adams & Barnard, Deptford	May 1783	26 Mar 1785	23 Apr 1785	Deptford[2]	11 Jul 1809 wrecked on the African coast
Blonde	1783	Calhoun, Bursledon	Sep 1783	22 Jan 1787	19 Feb 1787	Portsmouth[2]	Jun 1798 troopship; Jun 1805 sold

Notes:

[F] fir built

[1] Spent about a month at Harwich before sailing to Chatham for final fitting out.

[2] Fitted for Ordinary.

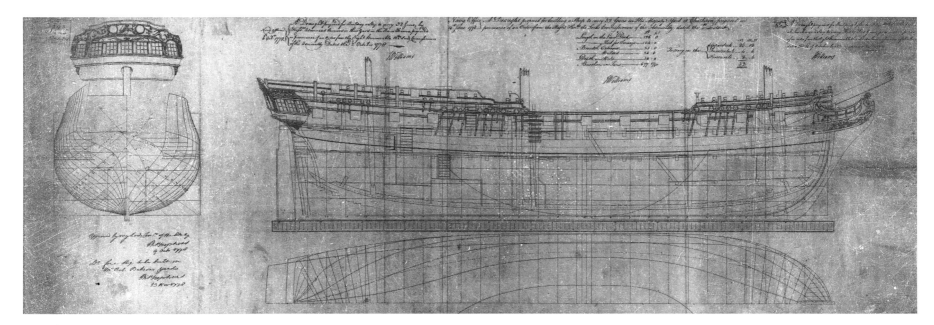

Amazon class of 1770, design sheer draught for ships ordered in 1778.
Essentially a finished version of the previous draught, the main interest in this drawing lies in the decorative detail and figurehead; the earliest mentioned ship is *Amphion* so the figure may represent this mythological hero.

Active class of 1778, design sheer & profile.
Very similar to the *Amazon* class, Edward Hunt's *Active*s had a slightly sharper midsection. The draught displays sweep ports, which are not found on the *Amazon* class draughts. Note the lightly indicated extended head modified during design.

response was quick, and eight days later it gave its opinion, backed with two completed draughts, that ships of the proposed size should be built strong enough for 18pdrs. Two 38s and a 36 armed with this calibre were ordered immediately and thus for once the Royal Navy took the initiative in introducing a new and more costly warship type.[28]

The full story of the 18pdr frigate belongs to another volume in this series, but the Admiralty's decision prefigures not only the extinction of the 28 but also gives the first hint of dissatisfaction with the standard 12pdr frigate. For three years no more 28s were built as intended, but the number of *Amazon*s increased steadily, although only two more of Hunt's *Active*s were ordered. By this stage of the war, Britain faced not

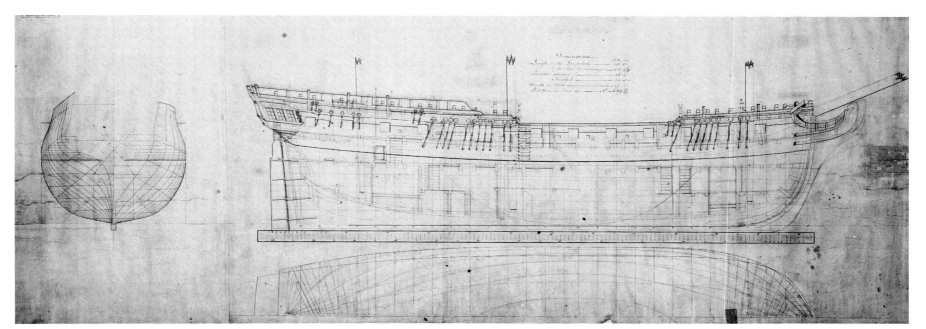

only France but also Spain and Holland, and was substantially out-numbered at sea for the first time since the 1690s. Numbers of ships became an overriding priority and the Navy Board embarked on a desperate search for shipbuilding capacity and was prepared to look in places previously considered too remote for satisfactory official monitoring. Whereas the Admiralty had been wont to specify the numbers of ships to be contracted, by 1779 almost every offer made to the Navy Board by shipbuilders was eagerly pursued. In 1782 they even accepted a private-venture frigate from Henry Adams – unthinkable under normal circumstances – but the ship was purchased in frame so that the *Heroine*, as she became, could at least be finished to Navy standards. Early in 1780 Hunt produced a new, lengthened 32-gun design destined to be built largely in what the Navy Board referred to as the 'out-ports', in this case Bristol and Liverpool. For this design he reverted to the more rounded midship section that could trace its ultimate inspiration back to the *Tygre*. However, even the increased length did not amount to breaking the time-hardened mould, for the new draught's proportions were a very close approximation to Slade's *Lowestoffe*, for which this class may be regarded as a replacement.

From about 1780 the Admiralty had shown a marked lack of enthusiasm for the work of the current Surveyors: for the all-important 74s, Williams's designs were not employed after 1774 and only one Hunt-designed ship was laid down after 1779. Instead the Admiralty preferred to revive Slade designs (and one by Bately) that were a generation old, constructing eighteen ships to four different draughts. The frigates were not so obviously deficient, but when the 28-gun class was resurrected in 1782, it is not surprising to find the long run of sister

Table 26: *ACTIVE* CLASS 32-GUN FIFTH RATES
Specification

Armament:	Upper deck	Quarterdeck	Forecastle	Guns	Men
Design	26 x 12pdrs	4 x 6pdrs	2 x 6pdrs	32	220
		12 x ½pdr swivels			
Added by AO					
10 Aug 1779		6 x 18pdr carr	2 x 18pdr carr		
25 Dec 1779[1]		4 x 18pdr carr	2 x 18pdr carr		
19 Nov 1794		4 x 24pdr carr	2 x 24pdr carr		

Designed by Sir Edward Hunt

	Lower deck ft ins	Keel ft ins	Breadth ft ins	Depth in hold ft ins	Burthen tons
Design	126 0	103 9⅝	35 4	12 2	689²⁵⁄₉₄
As completed					
Daedalus	125 7	103 1	35 8	11 10¾	702⁶⁰⁄₉₄
Mermaid	126 2½	103 9¾	35 5	11 11	692⁵⁹⁄₉₄
Cerberus	126 3½	104 2	35 7	12 2	701
Active	126 0	103 9⅞	35 7	12 2	697
Fox	126 2¼	104 1	35 5¾	12 2	697
Astraea	126 0	103 7⅜	35 9	12 0	703⁴⁴⁄₉₄
Ceres	126 3½	104 2	35 7	11 11½	692
Quebec	126 3	104 2	35 6½	12 1½	699

Notes:
[1] Actual as opposed to established numbers of carronades, where known, are given in Table 44.

Table 27: *ACTIVE* CLASS 32-GUN FIFTH RATES
Building Data

Name	Ordered	Builder	Laid Down	Launched	Sailed	Fitted at	Fate
Daedalus	25 Jun 1778	Fisher, Liverpool	Jul 1778	20 May 1780	[1]	Liverpool	Oct 1803 Trinity House hulk; July 1811 BU
Mermaid	27 Aug 1778	Sheerness Dyd[2]	29 Jul 1782	29 Nov 1784	30 Dec 1784	Sheerness	Nov 1815 BU
Cerberus	14 Oct 1778	Randall, Rotherhithe	24 Nov 1778	15 Jun 1779	25 Jul 1779	Deptford	30 Apr 1783 wrecked off Bermuda
Active	10 Dec 1778	Raymond, Northam	Feb 1779	30 Aug 1780	18 Nov 1780	Portsmouth	Jul 1796 wrecked in St Lawrence
Fox	10 Dec 1778	Parsons, Bursledon	Feb 1779	2 Jun 1780	27 Jul 1780	Portsmouth	1812 troopship; Apr 1816 BU
Astraea	7 May 1779	Fabian, East Cowes	Sep 1779	24 Jul 1781	19 Sep 1781	Portsmouth	1800-1805 troopship; 23 Mar 1808 wrecked
Ceres	7 May 1779	Fearon & Webb, Liverpool	4 Sep 1779	19 Sep 1781	11 Feb 1782	Liverpool	1804 slop ship; Mar 1830 BU
Quebec		Stares & Parsons, Bursledon	Jun 1780	24 May 1781	8 Aug 1781	Portsmouth	1813 hulked; July 1816 BU

Although *Daedalus* was the first ordered, they were known officially as the *Active* class, probably because they were listed alphabetically in their first Progress Book entry.
Notes:
[1] Coppered in Jun 1780 but exact sailing date not recorded.
[2] Laid down at Woolwich Dyd in Sep 1778 but was moved to Sheerness by AO of 21 Mar 1782 to allow the building of a 74; restarted as above.

Mermaid **of 1784, contemporary model.**

**Shown ready for launching, the model resembles the draught quite closely,
except for the raised waist and flush gangways; since the ship's launch was
delayed until 1784, two years after the standing order to make gangways flush
was issued, it may well represent the ship as completed. *Mermaid* is not known
to have had carronades before 1793, so even the open quarterdeck rails may be
correct as there was a tendency to remove the solid bulwarks in peacetime.**

ships to Williams's *Enterprize* being interrupted by two ships 'similar to
Milford' (*ie* Slade's modification of the *Unicorn*). The reintroduction of
the 28 is almost certainly a reaction to the shortage of shipbuilding
capacity, since the new orders all went to small yards in the Dover area
incapable of building larger craft; in fact, the contract for *Laurel* proved
too much for her builder, who went bankrupt and the ship was then
cancelled.

One very influential factor tending to offset the lacklustre sailing
qualities of the new frigates was the widespread introduction of copper

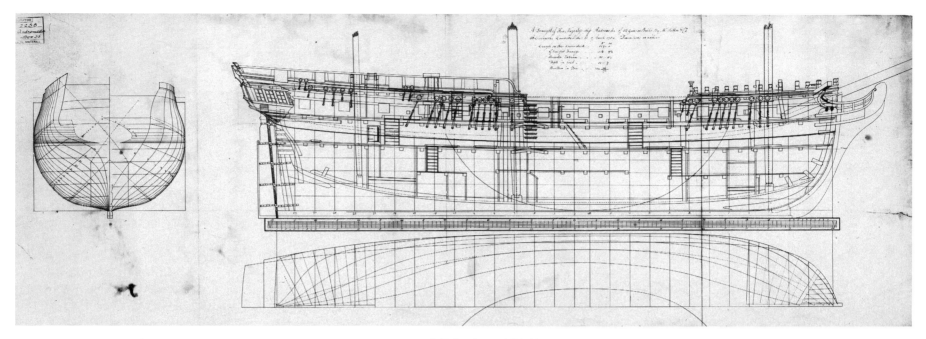

Andromeda of 1784, as fitted sheer & profile draught.

A lengthened version of the *Active*s, with a slightly modified hull form, by the time the *Andromeda* class was designed the carronade was already established as quarterdeck and forecastle armament; moreover, before the ship was launched the waist had been ordered raised (shown in a dotted line).

Table 28: *ANDROMEDA* CLASS 32-GUN FIFTH RATES
Specification

Armament:	Upper deck	Quarterdeck	Forecastle	Guns	Men
Design	26 x 12pdrs	4 x 6pdrs	2 x 6pdrs	32	220
		12 x ½pdr swivels			

Added by AO			
10 Aug 1779	6 x 18pdr carr	2 x 18pdr carr
25 Dec 1779[1]	4 x 18pdr carr	2 x 18pdr carr
19 Nov 1794	4 x 24pdr carr	2 x 24pdr carr

Designed by Sir Edward Hunt

	Lower deck	Keel	Breadth	Depth in hold	Burthen
	ft ins	ft ins	ft ins	ft ins	tons
Design	129 0	107 0	35 4	12 10	710 48/94
As completed					
Hermione	129 0	106 10½	35 5½	12 8	714 84/94
Druid	129 1¼	107 1⅜	35 5⅛	12 8	717 57/94
Andromeda	129 0	106 9¾	35 5½	12 7	714 36/94
Penelope	129 4	107 6	35 6	12 7	720 48/94
Aquilon	129 2	107 0	35 8	12 7½	724
Blanche	129 0	107 0	35 7½	12 7	722 48/94

Notes:
[1] Actual as opposed to established numbers of carronades, where known, are given in Table 44.

sheathing into the fleet in the 1770s. Ships had always been sheathed and/or payed in some form,[29] partly to protect the bottom from the destructive effects of marine borers like *teredo navalis*, but primarily to retard the growth of encrustation. Assuming the same level of seamanship, no single factor influenced performance as much as fouling, and with older methods of paying it was reckoned that a vessel needed to be cleaned every six weeks for maximum effect.[30] Copper sheathing not only gave a ship a speed advantage (all other things being equal, about 1-1½kts), but more importantly preserved this advantage for longer. This functioned in modern parlance as a 'force multiplier' so that ships spent less time in dock and more on active service, which was the equivalent of having a far larger uncoppered fleet. It is impossible to exaggerate the advantage of copper sheathing to the Royal Navy in this war, but it did nothing to inspire innovation in ship design and may have actually disguised its mediocrity.

If the Admiralty was dissatisfied with the quality of its cruiser design during this war, the concern did not manifest itself in the traditional interest in foreign prizes. Not only French, but Spanish, Dutch and some of the new American frigates fell into Royal Navy hands during the war, but at the time not one inspired a British derivative. Dutch ships were rather old-fashioned, with almost the proportions of earlier two-deckers, while Spanish ships were regarded as far too large for the puny armament carried; some of the American vessels were surprisingly

Table 29: *ANDROMEDA* CLASS 32-GUN FIFTH RATES
Building data

Name	Ordered	Builder	Laid Down	Launched	Sailed	Fitted at	Fate
Hermione	20 Mar 1780	Least & Tombe, Bristol	Jun 1780	9 Sep 1782	Jan 1783	Bristol	22 Sep 1797 turned over to Spanish after mutiny; 25 Oct 1799 recaptured, renamed *Retaliation*, then *Retribution*; 1805 BU
Druid	20 Mar 1780	Least & Tombe, Bristol	Aug 1780	16 Jun 1783	11 Nov 1783	Plymouth	Apr 1798 troopship; Oct 1813 BU
Andromeda		Sutton, Liverpool	May 1781	21 Apr 1784	[1]	Plymouth	1808 hulked; 1811 BU
Penelope		Burton, Liverpool	Feb 1782	27 Oct 1783	9 Feb 1784	Plymouth	Nov 1797 BU at Chatham
Aquilon		Young & Woolcombe, Thames	Nov 1782	23 Nov 1786	21 Dec 1786	Deptford	Sep 1815 BU
Blanche		Calhoun, Bursledon	Jul 1783	10 Jul 1786	[2]	Portsmouth	1799 troopship; 28 Sep 1799 wrecked

Although *Hermione* was the first ordered, they were known officially as the *Andromeda* class, probably because they were listed alphabetically in their first Progress Book entry.

Notes:

[1] Sailed to Plymouth 11 July 1784; fitted for Ordinary.

[2] Sailed to Portsmouth 12 Jul 1786; coppered and fitted for Ordinary.

Table 30: *HEROINE* CLASS 32-GUN FIFTH RATE
Specification

Armament:	Upper deck	Quarterdeck	Forecastle	Guns	Men
Design	26 x 12pdrs	4 x 6pdrs	2 x 6pdrs	32	220
Added by AO					
31 Jan 1793		6 x 18pdr carr			

Designed by builder and 'purchased in her frame'

	Lower deck	Keel	Breadth	Depth in hold	Burthen
	ft ins	ft ins	ft ins	ft ins	tons
Design	131 4½	108 10½	36 10½	13 1	787⁴⁷⁄₉₄
As completed					
Heroine	130 11½	107 6⅜	36 10¼	13 0	779

well designed (*Iris*, ex-*Hancock*, was a particular favourite), but were compromised by the haste and lightness of their construction; this left only the French and none of their big 12pdr frigates was regarded as a suitable model, perhaps because the Royal Navy had already decided to abandon the calibre for all future frigates.

Heroine of 1783, fitting out draught (right).

A copy of this draught was sent to the builder in May 1782 to fit out the ship to Navy Board standards; even so, the carronade ports appear to be afterthoughts. This private-venture frigate had a much rounder section than any Navy-designed ship but was their equal in performance and superior in some respects, such as load freeboard.

Virginia, 28, ex-American, captured 1778, as fitted sheer & profile taken off, November 1782.

One of the smaller Continental frigates of the original 1776 programme, *Virginia* was rated as a 28 in the Royal Navy because she carried a main armament of twenty-four 9pdrs despite being the same size as a British 32. Although a sharp model, her surviving Sailing Quality Reports suggest that the ship was only a moderate performer. The beakhead bulkhead was a rather old-fashioned feature by the 1770s.

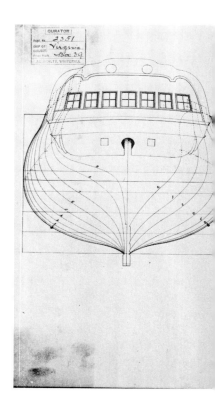

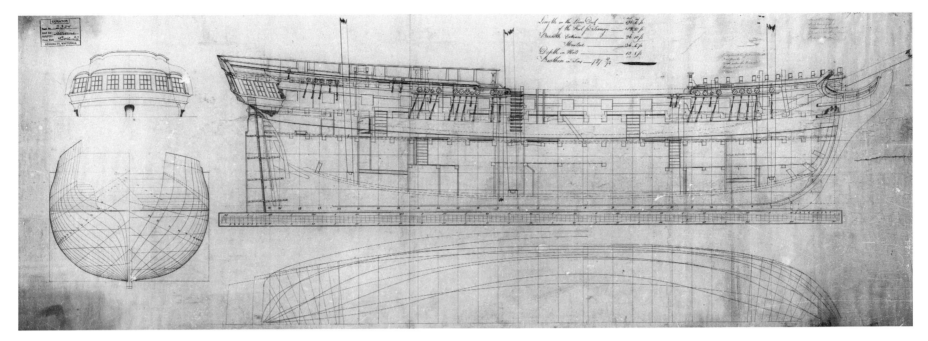

Table 31: HEROINE CLASS 32-GUN FIFTH RATE
Building Data

Name	Ordered	Builder	Laid Down	Launched	Sailed	Fitted at	Fate
Heroine	Purchased 1782	Adams, Bucklers Hard		Aug 1783	11 Oct 1783	Portsmouth	1803 floating battery; Feb 1806 sold

Exact dates are not recorded for purchase and launch, but the armament was established by AO of 17 May 1782 and the ship sailed to Portsmouth on 17 August 1783, so she must have been purchased and launched respectively before these dates.

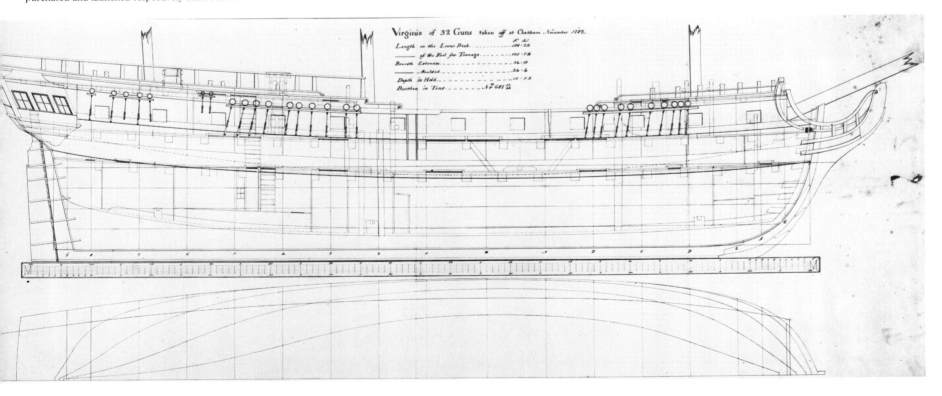

Table 32: CAPTURED SHIPS 1776-1783

Name, rate	Nationality	Built	Captured	Dimensions Lower deck	Keel	Breadth	Depth in hold	Burthen	Armament Upper deck	Quarter-deck	Fore-castle	Fate
				ft ins	ft ins	ft ins	ft ins	tons	(No x cal)	(No x cal)	(No x cal)	
Equivalents of English 28s												
Delaware, 28 ex-US 24	US	Philadelphia, 1776	27 Sep 1777	117 9½	98 0¼	32 10½	9 8½	564	'28 guns, 9pdrs' 22 x 12	6 x 6		14 Apr 1783 sold
Virginia, 28	US	Baltimore, 1776	May 1778	126 3½	108 0	34 6	10 7	681 53/94	'28 guns, 9pdrs'[1]			Dec 1782 BU
Albemarle, 28 ex-*Menagère*	Fr flûte	Rochefort, 1775	1778	125 3½	102 0⅝	31 7¼	13 7½	543 6/94	28 guns, 8pdrs[2]			1 Jun 1784 sold
Hinchinbrook, 28 ex-*Astrée*	Fr	1778	1779	115 0		33 3		557	[2]			19 Jan 1782 foundered
Grana, 28	Sp	Ferrol, 1778	25 Feb 1781	117 10	97 0	31 11¾	9 4	527 60/94	[2] 22 x 6	6 x 4	2 x 4 brass	Sep 1806 sold
Equivalents of English 32s												
Iris, 32 ex-*Hancock*	US	Newburyport, 1776	7 Jul 1777	137 1	116 6	34 3¾	10 11	730	26 x 12 24 x 12	4 x 6 8 x 6	2 x 6 2 x 6	11 Sep 1781 captured by French
Licorne, 36	Fr	Brest, 1755	18 Jun 1778	127 1	106 7½	34 7½	10 6¼	680	26 x 12[3] ?8pdrs	8 x 6	2 x 6	2 Dec 1783 sold
Convert, 32 ex-*Pallas*	Fr	St Malo, 1777	19 Jun 1778	127 9	106 2⅛	35 4¼	13 9¼	706	26 x 9 26 x 12	4 x 4 4 x 6	2 x 4 2 x 6	1791 BU
Sartine, 32	Fr	1776	25 Aug 1778	132 6	118 0	35 9	15 3	802	?8pdrs[2]			26 Nov 1780 wrecked
Raleigh, 32	US	Portsmouth, NH, 1776	27 Sep 1778	131 5	110 7½	34 5	11 0	697	26 x 12[4] 26 x 12	4 x 6 8 x 6	2 x 6 2 x 6	17 Jul 1783 sold
Oiseau, 32	Fr	1769	13 Jan 1779	146 3	126 9⅝	34 1	9 10¾	784	26 x 9 ?8pdrs	4 x 6	2 x 6	19 Jun 1783 sold
Danae, 32	Fr East India Co ship	Lorient, 1758	13 May 1779	129 3	107 2	34 9	10 6¼	689	26 x 9	4 x 6	2 x 6	Oct 1797 sold
Alcmene, 32	Fr	Toulon, 1774	21 Oct 1779	131 0	111 1¾	35 8	11 6	731	26 x 9 26 x 8	2 x 6 4 x 4	4 x 6 2 x 4	19 Aug 1784 sold
Providence, 32 ex-28	US	Providence, RI, 1776	12 May 1780	126 6½	104 10⅜	33 8	10 5	632	[2]			11 Mar 1784 sold
Clinton, 32 ex-*Esperance*	Fr	1779	30 Sep 1780	134 0	113 0	35 0	13 9	736	[2] 26 x 12	2 x 6		5 Jul 1784 sold
Proselyte, 32 ex-*Stanislas*, 26	Fr privateer	Le Havre, 1780	Dec 1780	134 9¼	114 9½	33 6½	10 9	689	[2]			10 Feb 1785 sold
Mars, 32 ex-38	Du	?	3 Feb 1781	130 9	108 10	34 10	11 10	703	[2]			25 Mar 1784 sold
Aimable, 32	Fr	Toulon, 1776	19 Apr 1782	133 5	109 5	36 8	11 0	782	26 x 12 26 x 8	4 x 6 4 x 4	2 x 6 2 x 4	May 1814 BU
Concorde, 32	Fr	Rochefort, 1777	15 Feb 1783	142 11	118 10	37 6	11 7	888 82/94	26 x 12 28 x 12	4 x 6 4 x 6	2 x 6 2 x 6	22 Jan 1811 sold

Name, rate	Nationality	Built	Captured	Dimensions					Armament			Fate
				Lower deck	Keel	Breadth	Depth in hold	Burthen	Upper deck	Quarter-deck	Fore-castle	
				ft ins	*ft ins*	*ft ins*	*ft ins*	*tons*	*(No x cal)*	*(No x cal)*	*(No x cal)*	
Larger than English 32s												
Prudente, 36 ex-32	Fr	St Malo, 1777	2 Jun 1779	136 0	118 11	37 9¾	10 10	897	26 x 12	10 x 6	2 x 6 [5]	1803 sold
Santa Monica, 36 ex-34	Sp	Cartagena, 1777	Jul 1779	145 0½	122 0⅞	38 8	11 10	956 18/94	26 x 12	8 x 9	2 x 6	28 Mar 1782 wrecked
Santa Margarita, 36 ex-34	Sp	Ferrol, 1774	11 Nov 1779	145 6	123 6⅛	38 10½	11 8½	993	26 x 12	8 x 6	2 x 6	1817 quarantine ship; 8 Sep 1836 sold
Fortunée, 36 ex-32	Fr	Brest, 1777	22 Dec 1779	141 3	124 5	38 1¼	12 1	948	28 x 12 / 26 x 12	10 x 6 / 4 x 6	2 x 6 / 2 x 6	Oct 1785 convict ship; BU c1800
Monsieur, 36	Fr privateer	1779	2 May 1780	139 2¼	115 3⅜	36 6½	17 9½	819	26 x 12	8 x 6	2 x 6	25 Sep 1783 sold
Belle Poule, 36 ex-32	Fr	Bordeaux, 1765	17 Jul 1780	140 0	118 7⅛	37 10	11 11	903	26 x 12 / 26 x 12	8 x 6 / 4 x 6	2 x 6 / 2 x 6	14 Sep 1801 sold
Nymphe, 36 ex-32	Fr	Brest, 1777	10 Aug 1780	143 4	120 4½	38 3¼	11 9	938	26 x 12 / 26 x 12	8 x 6 / 4 x 6	2 x 6 / 2 x 6	18 Dec 1810 wrecked
Confederate, 36 ex-*Confederacy*, 32	US	Norwich, Conn, 1778	14 Apr 1781	154 9		37 0	12 3	970 36/94	2, 6			Mar 1782 BU
Santa Leocadia, 36 ex-34	Sp	Ferrol, 1777	1 May 1781	144 10	119 8⅛	38 8	11 7¼	951 67/94	26 x 12 [7]	8 x 6	2 x 6	23 Sep 1794 sold
Magicienne, 32 ex-32	Fr	Toulon, 1777	2 Sep 1781	143 9	118 4½	39 2½	12 1½	967 74/94	26 x 12 / 26 x 12	4 x 6 / 4 x 6	2 x 6 / 2 x 6	27 Aug 1810 burnt to avoid capture

The table includes only those ships taken into British service. Armament is as fitted for British service; the second is as captured, where recorded; changes, where known, are given in Table 45.

Notes:

[1] A late-war list gives 24 x 9pdrs only.

[2] Assume the standard armament for the rate applies if no specific battery is quoted.

[3] Changed to 9pdrs and 4pdrs by Navy Board warrant of 2 Nov 1778.

[4] On 1 Sep 1779 it was proposed to fit short 18pdrs until 12s became available.

[5] Rated 36 and later 38; upperworks armament changed frequently – an AO of 30 Dec 1779 gives 10 x 6pdrs and 8 x 18pdr carronades but an AO of 25 Jan 1780 allows 2 x 12pdrs to replace 2 x 6pdrs on the forecastle and no carronades there; by AO of 9 Aug 1780 2 x 6pdrs replaced two quarterdeck carronades.

[6] Log makes it clear that the ship was armed with 12pdrs.

[7] One Dimensions Book list gives 18pdrs, but AO of 19 Sep 1781 specifies the above.

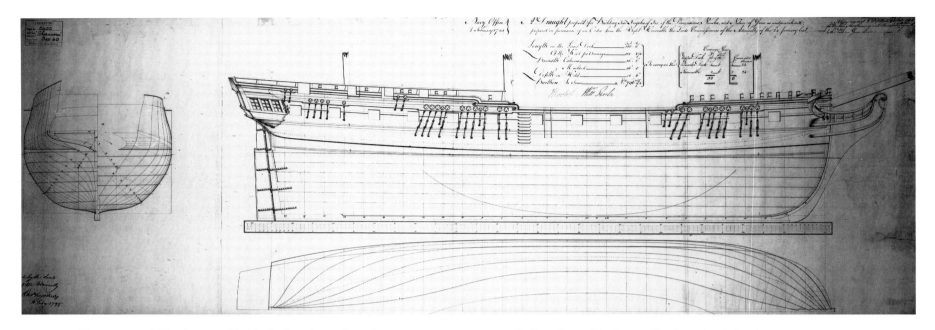

Shannon and Maidstone of 1795, design sheer draught.

These ships were not a separate class but only a version of the contemporary 18pdr-armed 32s of the *Alcmene* class modified for softwood construction (one of the few visible differences, the square tuck stern, can be seen in the body plan). The change of mind about the armament is also apparent in the rubric of the draught where under upper deck armament the calibre of '18' has been erased and replaced with '12'. Note the austerity billet head in place of a figure.

Pallas class of 1792, profile draught (below).

A copy of this draught was sent to Deptford on 19 March 1795 for *Shannon* and *Maidstone* but a note specifies that they were fitted with the enlarged quarterdeck ports (for carronades) indicated in red on the original; the red lines also suggest that the bulwark was extended to the main mast at the same time. These alterations are also marked on the sheer draught.

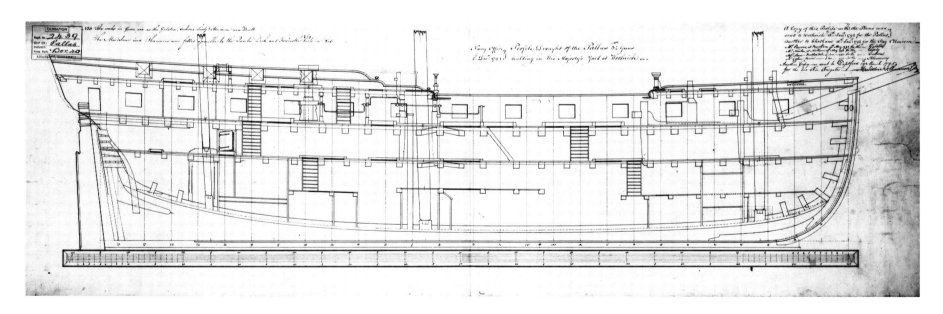

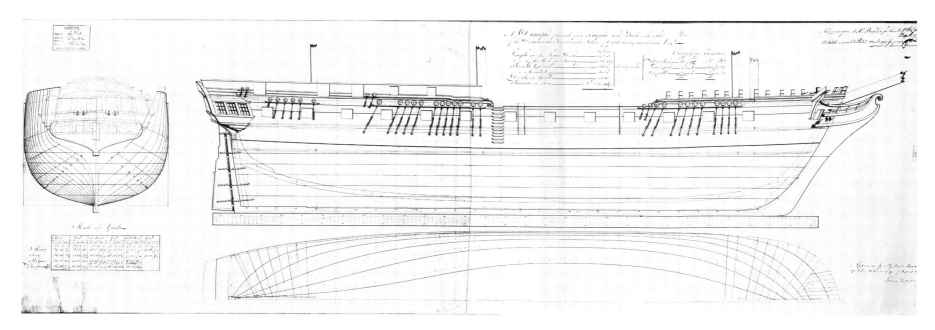

Triton of 1796, design sheer draught.

The most singular frigate design of the period, *Triton*'s unique bow lines and almost total absence of sheer are striking features. Also unusual is the absence of a designer's signature anywhere on the sheer or profile, although Henslow's and Rule's initials endorse the deck plans. Like *Maidstone* and *Shannon*, she was originally intended for 18pdrs, the original entry on the rubric being scored through and replaced with 12s.

Table 33: *MAIDSTONE* CLASS 32-GUN FIFTH RATES
Specification

Armament:	Upper deck	Quarterdeck	Forecastle	Guns	Men
Design	26 x 12pdrs	4 x 6pdrs	2 x 6pdrs	32	240
		4 x 24pdr carr	2 x 24pdr carr		

Designed by Sir John Henslow; fir-built variant of *Alcmene* class 18pdr 32s

	Lower deck	Keel	Breadth	Depth in hold	Burthen
	ft ins	ft ins	ft ins	ft ins	tons
Design	135 0	112 4½	36 6	12 6	796 $^{17}/_{94}$
As completed					
Maidstone	135 1	112 4⅜	36 8	12 5	804
Shannon	135 0¼	112 3¼	36 8	12 4¾	803

By the end of her career *Maidstone*'s quarterdeck and forecastle armament was 8 x 24pdr carronades and 4 x 24pdr carronades respectively.

Table 34: **MAIDSTONE CLASS 32-GUN FIFTH RATES**
Building Data

Name	Ordered	Builder	Laid Down	Launched	Sailed	Fitted at	Fate
Maidstone	4 Feb 1795	Deptford Dyd	Mar 1795	12 Dec 1795		Deptford	1810 BU
Shannon	4 Feb 1795	Deptford Dyd	Apr 1795	9 Feb 1796		Deptford	May 1802 sold

6. *The Last 12pdr Ships*

The conclusion of the War of American Independence marked the end of both the 9pdr and the 12pdr armed frigate, effectively eclipsed by the more potent 18pdr ships. The demise of the 28 had been intended in 1778 and its short-lived revival was purely a matter of wartime exigencies. On the other hand, there appears to have been no conscious directive to abandon the 12pdr type, but as preparations were made for a possible breach with Spain in 1790, the new 32-gun *Pallas* class was designed for 18pdrs, with no apparent consideration being given to the smaller calibre. No new 12pdr designs were produced thereafter, and the few 12pdr ships commissioned were rearmed versions of classes originally intended for 18pdrs.

The three ships of Henslow's *Pallas* class were followed in 1793 by a version modified to incorporate 6in more beam. Two further additions to this four-ship *Alcmene* class in 1795 were ordered to be built from fir, but because of doubts about their relative strength, *Maidstone* and *Shannon* were established with twenty-six 12pdrs instead of their half-sisters' 18s. However, two pairs of fir-built examples of the current larger 36- and 38-gun designs ordered on the same day retained the 18pdr main battery.

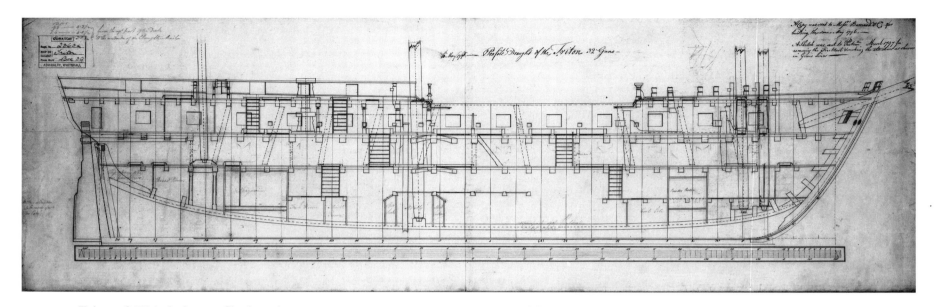

Triton of 1796, design profile draught.

Dated 10 May 1796, the profile shows the alteration to the fore mast ordered in March 1797, and also indicates sweep ports, which are not on the sheer. The trim of this ship may have been critical – unusually, she was designed to float on an even keel – and compartments at the extremities of the ship at platform level are marked 'This space to be kept free from all kinds of stores'.

Triton of 1796, contemporary model.

A simplified but accurate model of the ship before the fore mast was moved forward; the gangways have been raised as indicated in dotted lines on the sheer draught.

Undoubtedly the oddest frigate of the 1790s was the experimental fir-built *Triton*, whose design is credited to the 'Admiralty'. A wall-sided vessel with virtually no sheer to the decks and a sharp overhanging bow, the ship appears to be more of an exercise in economising on curved compass timber than an attempt at an improved hull-form (although her mast and spar dimensions had to be calculated specially, suggesting some acknowledgement of her unique lines). Originally designed for 18pdrs, she too was ordered to carry 12s during construction. She was none too successful and was confined to harbour service from 1800.[31]

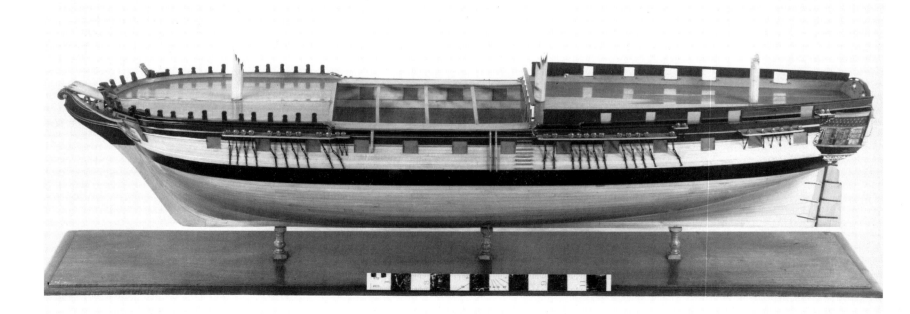

Table 35: *TRITON* CLASS 32-GUN FIFTH RATE
Specification

Armament:	Upper deck	Quarterdeck	Forecastle	Guns	Men
Design	26 x 18pdrs	4 x 6pdrs	2 x 6pdrs	32	240
		6 x 24pdr carr	2 x 24pdr carr		
Altered during design to					
	26 x 12pdrs	As above	As above		

Design attributed to 'Admiralty'; fir-built

	Lower deck	Keel	Breadth	Depth in hold	Burthen
	ft ins	ft ins	ft ins	ft ins	tons
Design	142 0	123 1⅜	36 0	11 10	848⁶⁶/₉₄
As completed					
Triton	142 0	123 0⅛	36 2	11 10½	852

Notes:
Carried 12 x 9pdrs and 10 x 24pdr carronades on the upper deck and no other guns on harbour service after 1800.

Circe class of 1804, design sheer draught.

The draught mentions all the ships of the class. Minor modifications during design include the raising of the waist gangways, the opening to carronade size of the ports in the wake of the main and fore shrouds (originally intended for 6pdr long guns), and an alteration to the pattern of lights in the stern – the original *Richmond* class had had five narrow windows with those to the quarter galleries 'blind', but this was changed by order of 10 September 1804 to six wider lights with one in each gallery (although these were usually false).

Table 36: *TRITON* CLASS 32-GUN FIFTH RATE
Building Data

Name	Ordered	Builder	Laid Down	Launched	Sailed	Fitted at	Fate
Triton	7 Apr 1796	Barnard, Deptford	Apr 1796	5 Sep 1796		Deptford	1800 hulked; 3 Nov 1814

Notes:
The order date is the day of Admiralty approval and signature of the contract.

The final manifestation of the 12pdr frigate was equally bizarre. In 1804 a whole class of frigates was laid down to the lines of Bately's *Richmond* class of 1756; they had the modern trappings of built-up bulwarks and an austerity fiddlehead, but not only were the lines unchanged but the draught even shows the oarports of the originals. The contemporary historian William James[32] claimed that it was the breaking up of the *Thames* in 1803 that brought the class to the Admiralty's attention (and there are precedents for this) but it was part of a wider return to earlier (and hence smaller) designs that has been associated with the administration of the Earl of St Vincent.

As First Lord in the period after the Peace of Amiens in 1801, St Vincent was bent on a policy of economy and dockyard reform. Naturally, few ships were ordered at this time, but there was one class of frigates and this utilised a design of 1780 – it is no coincidence that this happened to be the smallest existing 18pdr armed class.[33] However, the expected long peace soon collapsed and the ensuing mobilisation revealed, among other deficiencies, a shortage of serviceable frigates. Unfortunately, St Vincent's attempted reform of the timber contracting procedure had led to a desperate shortage of timber stocks, and

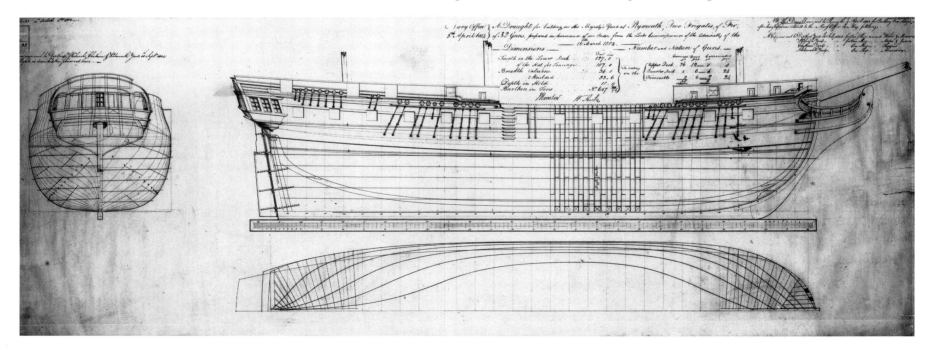

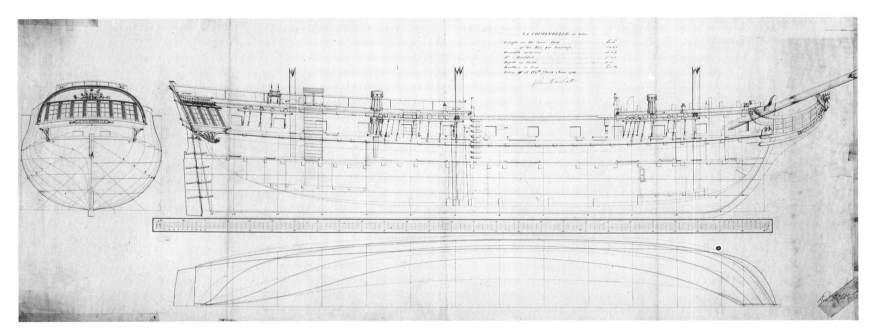

Table 37: *CIRCE* CLASS 32-GUN FIFTH RATES
Specification

Armament:	Upper deck	Quarterdeck	Forecastle	Guns	Men
Design	26 x 12pdrs	2 x 6pdrs	2 x 6pdrs	32	220
		6 x 24pdr carr	2 x 24pdr carr		
As completed	26 x 12pdrs	8 x 24pdr carr	4 x 24pdr carr		

Modified version of Bately's *Richmond* class of 1756, with round bow, thirteen upper deck gunports, and framing adapted for fir construction

	Lower deck	Keel	Breadth	Depth in hold	Burthen
	ft ins	ft ins	ft ins	ft ins	tons
Design	127 0	107 4	34 0	11 9	657 88/94
As completed					
Circe	127 0	106 10⅞	34 4	11 9	670
Pallas	127 1	107 1	34 2	11 10	667
Thames	127 1	107 0¾	34 1	11 9	661
Jason	127 1	107 0⅞	34 1	11 9	661
Hebe	127 0½	107 0	34 0	11 9	658
Minerva	127 0	107 0	34 10½	11 3½	659
Alexandria	127 0¾	107 0	34 1¼	11 9	662
Medea	Cancelled				

Notes:
The above 'as completed' armament seems to have been carried by all the ships of this class.

Tourterelle, 28, ex-French, as captured sheer & profile draught, taken off at Plymouth, June 1795.

France ceased to build 8pdr-armed frigates in 1774 but at the beginning of their involvement in the American War reintroduced the calibre for a new class of large corvettes measuring about 640 tons. Except for their formal rating, they were in every respect small frigates; by the 1790s the main armament had grown from twenty to twenty-four 8pdrs and some later vessels like *Tourterelle* also carried six 4pdrs *sur les gaillards*. Captured examples of these vessels usually rated as 28s in British service.

particularly English oak, in the Dockyards.[34] In the circumstances, therefore, there was little alternative to the traditional stop-gap measure of softwood ships built in the Royal Dockyards and so before it left office in May 1804, St Vincent's Admiralty Board decided on this approach for a class of the smallest viable frigates, primarily to economise on timber but also have them at sea as quickly as possible.[35] Employing such an old design was not without its problems, for the Navy Board had to admit that the design process had been held up by the difficulty of finding the original *Richmond* class draughts.

The possibility of invasion was a major preoccupation in the years leading up to Trafalgar, and this only served to reinforce the traditional British strategic emphasis on quantity above individual quality (for 'quality' read 'size' in most circumstances). To give another example, the 9pdr armed small Sixth Rate (nominally 22 guns) was also revived at this time after a lapse of over twenty years, suggesting a desire for an even more economical frigate-substitute. Before 1804 there was a wide gap in new building between the largest sloop at about 450 tons and the smallest frigate at about 900 tons which both the 22s and the 32s were designed to fill. However, in the right hands, even these apparently outclassed small ships could be useful, as Lord Cochrane's famous 'Flying *Pallas*' was amply to demonstrate.

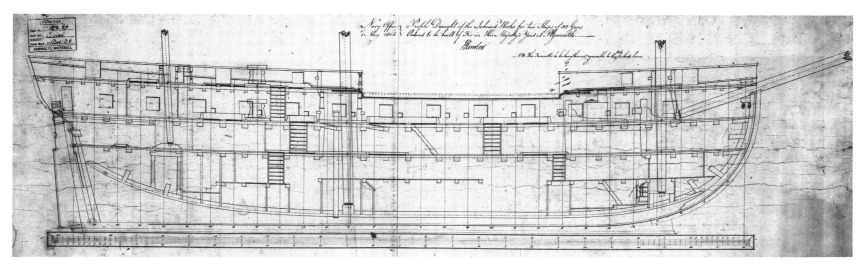

Circe class of 1804, design profile draught.

This draught shows the sweep ports missing from the sheer and notes the extension of the forecastle and the raising of the waist.

Table 38: *CIRCE* CLASS 32-GUN FIFTH RATES *Building Data*

Name	Ordered	Builder	Laid Down	Launched	Sailed	Fitted at	Fate
Circe	16 Mar 1804	Plymouth Dyd	Jun 1804	17 Nov 1804	13 Feb 1805	Plymouth	20 Aug 1814 sold
Pallas	16 Mar 1804	Plymouth Dyd	Jun 1804	17 Nov 1804	21 Jan 1805	Plymouth	18 Dec 1810 wrecked in Firth of Forth
Thames	12 Jul 1804	Chatham Dyd	Jul 1804	24 Oct 1805	8 Jan 1806	Chatham	Oct 1816 BU
Jason	12 Jul 1804	Woolwich Dyd	Aug 1804	21 Nov 1804	18 Jan 1805	Woolwich	Jul 1815 BU at Plymouth
Hebe	12 Jul 1804	Deptford Dyd	Aug 1804	31 Dec 1804	27 Feb 1805	Deptford	28 Apr 1813 sold
Minerva	12 Jul 1804	Deptford Dyd	Aug 1804	25 Oct 1805	19 Dec 1805	Deptford	Feb 1815 BU
Alexandria	12 Jul 1804	Portsmouth Dyd	Oct 1804	18 Feb 1806	20 Apr 1806	Portsmouth	1817 hulked at Sheerness; Jul 1818 BU
Medea	12 Jul 1804	Chatham Dyd	Cancelled				

Notes: All built of fir, although James' *Naval History* (Vol III, p375) claims that *Thames* was constructed of old oak.

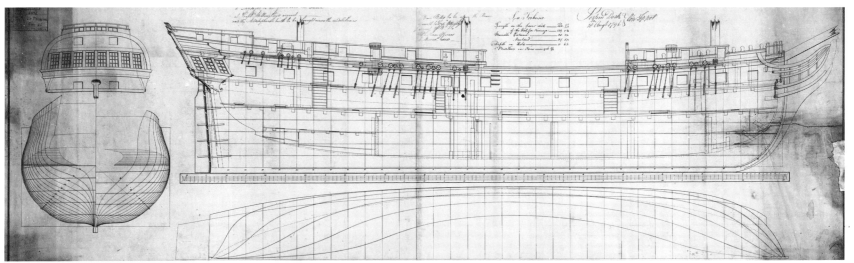

Tribune, 36, ex-French, as captured sheer & profile draught, taken off at Portsmouth, August 1796.

Just as France was slow to take up the 12pdr frigate, despite an early prototype, so she was slow to abandon the class. The great shipbuilding programme of 1786 envisaged sixty frigates, only a third of which were to be 18pdr-armed and the rest 12pdr ships, the lighter calibre being specified for some new construction until 1798. They had little chance in action against the increasing preponderance of 18pdr ships in the Royal Navy, despite their large size, and the 36-gun 12pdr category of the Navy List came to be almost entirely composed of prize ships. *Tribune* was one of the largest at 916 tons and one of the final generation, being launched at Rochefort in 1794.

Table 39: CAPTURED SHIPS 1793-1815

Name, rate	Nationality	Built	Captured	Dimensions					Armament			Fate
				Lower deck	Keel	Breadth	Depth in hold	Burthen	Upper deck	Quarterdeck	Forecastle	
				ft ins	ft ins	ft ins	ft ins	tons	(No x cal)	(No x cal)	(No x cal)	
Equivalents of English 28s												
Tourterelle, 28 ex-*24*	Fr	Honfleur, 1794	13 Mar 1795	125 11	108 3¼	31 9⅛	9 10	581	24 x 9	4 x 6, 4 x 24 carr	2 x 6, 2 x 24 carr	1816 sunk as breakwater
Surprise, 28 ex-*Unité*, 24[1]	Fr	Le Havre, 1794	20 Apr 1796	126 0	108 6⅛	31 8	10 8½	579	24 x 32 carr	8 x 18 carr	4 x 6	Feb 1802 sold
Braak, 28 ex-*Minerva*	Du	Zeeland, 17?	28 Aug 1799	116 6½	95 8⅛	34 8½	10 6	613	22 x 32 carr	2 x 6		1802 sold
Heldin, 28	Du	Amsterdam, 1796	28 Aug 1799	122 1	102 3⅝	34 2¼	11 4¾	636	24 x 12	4 x 6		1802 sold
Equivalents of English 32s												
Eurus, 32 ex-*Zefir*	Du	Amsterdam, 1786	6 Mar 1796	126 7½	107 8	35 0	12 6½	702	26 x 12	4 x 6	2 x 6	1799 troopship; 1803 storeship; 1834 BU
Janus, 32 ex-*Argo*	Du	Amsterdam, 1791	12 May 1796	131 0	108 0	35 0	11 10½	704	26 x 12	4 x 6, 4 x 24 carr	2 x 6, 2 x 24 carr	Jan 1798 hulked; 21 Feb 1811 sold
Proselyte, 32 ex-*Jason*	Du	Rotterdam, 1770	8 Jun 1796	133 1	110 8	35 8	12 0	748	26 x 12	4 x 6, 4 x 24 carr	2 x 6, 2 x 24 carr	4 Sep 1801 wrecked
Helder, 32	Du	Rotterdam, 1795	28 Aug 1799	127 0	103 4¾	37 5	13 0½	770	24 x 24 carr	8 x 18 carr		1803 floating battery; 1802 sold
Barbadoes, 32 ex-*Brave*[2]	Fr privateer	1801	May 1803	139 8	117 6½	35 2⅝	10 3	775	24 x 9	8 x 24 carr	2 x 6, 2 x 24 carr	28 Sep 1812 wrecked
Frederickstein, 32	Da	Copenhagen, 1800	7 Sep 1807	128 8	108 10	34 3	9 4	679	26 x 12	6 x 24 carr	2x6, 2x24 carr	Jun 1813 BU
Larger than English 32s												
Oiseau, 36 ex-*Cléopâtre*, 36	Fr	St Malo, 1781	18 Jan 1793	145 7¾	120 8⅞	37 8½	11 11¾	913	26 x 12 26 x 12	8 x 24 carr 8 x 6	2 x 6 2 x 6	1810 prison ship; 18 Sep 1816 sold
Lutine, 36	Fr	Toulon, 1779	29 Aug 1793	143 3	118 6	38 10	12 1½	950	26 x 12 26 x 12	4 x 6, 4 x 24 carr 8 x 6	2 x 6, 2 x 24 carr 2 x 6	9 Oct 1799 wrecked
Topaze, 38[3]	Fr	Toulon, 1789	Dec 1793	144 7	120 6¾	37 9¾	12 1	916	28 x 12	6 x 6, 6 x 32 carr	2 x 6, 2 x 32 carr	1 Sep 1814 sold
Réunion, 36	Fr	Toulon, 1786	20 Oct 1793	144 0	118 4⅜	38 10½	12 1	951	26 x 12	8 x 6	2 x 6	7 Dec 1793 wrecked
Espion, 36 ex-*Atalante*	Fr	Rochefort, 1784	7 May 1794	148 9	120 6	39 2	11 10½	983	26 x 12	4 x 6, 4 x 18 carr	2 x 6, 2 x 18 carr	1798 floating battery; 16 Nov 1799 wrecked
Pique, 34	Fr	Rochefort, 1785	6 Jan 1795	144 1½	119 5¼	37 9¼	11 8	906	26 x 12	6 x 6, 4 x 24 carr	2 x 6, 2 x 24 carr	2 Jul 1798 destroyed to prevent capture
Prévoyante, 36	Fr	Bayonne, 1773	17 May 1795	143 0	121 11½	35 2½	13 4	804	30 x 12	4 x 9, 8 x 18 carr	2 x 9, 2 x 18 carr	1801 storeship; 1819 sold
Unité, 32 ex-36	Fr	Rochefort, 1787	12 Apr 1796	142 5½	118 5½	37 8	11 0	893	26 x 12	4 x 6, 4 x 24 carr	2 x 6, 2 x 24 carr	May 1802 sold
Tribune, 34	Fr	Rochefort, 1794	8 Jun 1796	143 7½	119 0⅝	38 0½	11 6½	916	26 x 12	6 x 6, 6 x 32 carr	2 x 6, 2 x 32 carr	16 Nov 1797 wrecked
Renommée, 38	Fr	1793	20 Jul 1796	140 6½	119 4⅝	38 1½	11 7½	823	26 x 12	12 x 32 carr	2 x 9, 2 x 32 carr	1800 troopship; 1810 BU
Mahonesa, 36 ex-*34*	Sp	Mahon, 1789	13 Oct 1796	145 1	118 6¼	39 3¾	11 9½	974	26 x 12	6 x 6	2 x 6	Never cruised; 1798 BU

Name, rate	Nation-ality	Built	Captured	Dimensions									Armament			Fate
				Lower deck		Keel		Breadth		Depth in hold		Burthen	Upper deck	Quarterdeck	Forecastle	
				ft	ins	ft	ins	ft	ins	ft	ins	tons	(No x cal)	(No x cal)	(No x cal)	
Hamadryad, 36 ex-*Ninfa*, 34	Sp	Mahon, 1795	26 Apr 1797									890	26 x 12	8 x 6, 6 x 32 carr	2 x 6, 2 x 32 carr	24 Dec 1797 wrecked
Nereide, 36	Fr	St Malo, 1779	20 Dec 1797	139	11¼	118	10⅝	37	6¾	11	7	892	26 x 12 26 x 12	8 x 6, 4 x 24 carr 6 x 6	2 x 6, 2 x 24 carr 2 x 6	In French hands 28 Aug to 6 Dec 1810; then laid up until sold 1 Mar 1816
Santa Dorothea, 34	Sp	Ferrol, 1775	15 Jul 1798	146	9	110	4½	39	0	12	0	958	26 x 12 26 x 12	6 x 6, 6 x 24 carr 6 x 6	2 x 6, 2 x 24 carr 2 x 6	1802 laid up until Jun 1814, when BU, Portsmouth
Decade, 36	Fr	Bordeaux, 1794	24 Aug 1798	143	8½	119	1¼	38	0	11	8	914	26 x 12	6 x 6, 6 x 24 carr	4 x 6, 2 x 24 carr	21 Feb 1811 sold
Ambuscade, 36 ex-*Embuscade*	Fr	Rochefort, 1789	12 Oct 1798	142	4	120	0¾	37	8	11	6½	905	26 x 12	8 x 6, 6 x 32 carr	2 x 6, 2 x 32 carr	16 Jan 1804 renamed *Seine*; Aug 1813 BU
Wilhelmina, 32 ex-*Furie*	Du	Vlissingen, 1787	24 Oct 1798	133	0	109	1	37	9	12	4	827	26 x 12	4 x 6, 4 x 24 carr	2 x 6, 2 x 24 carr	1800 troopship; Jan 1813 sold at Penang
Santa Teresa, 30 ex-34	Sp	Ferrol, 1787	6 Feb 1799	143	10	120	7	38	6			952	26 x 12	2 x 6, 10 x 32 carr	2 x 6, 2 x 32 carr	Sep 1802 sold
Carmen, 36 ex-*N S del Carmen*, 34	Sp	Ferrol, 1770	7 Apr 1800	147	2	119	9	37	9	11	0	908	26 x 12	6 x 6	2 x 6	Feb 1802 sold
Florentina, 36 ex-*Santa Florentina*, 34	Sp	Cartagena, 1776	7 Apr 1800	146	8	119	6	37	8	10	6	902	26 x 12	6 x 6	2 x 6	1802 sold
Dédaigneuse, 36	Fr	Bayonne, 1797	28 Jan 1801	143	10½	119	9½	37	6¼	11	9	897	26 x 12	2 x 6, 10 x 24 carr	2 x 6, 2 x 24 carr	1810 receiving ship; 21 May 1823 sold
Chiffonne, 36	Fr	Nantes, 1799	19 Aug 1801	144	1	120	6¼	37	11	12	0	921	26 x 12	2 x 9, 10 x 32 carr	2 x 9, 2 x 32 carr	1 Sep 1814 sold
Alexandria, 36 ex-*Regenerée*	Fr	1793	2 Sep 1801	144	3	119	8½	37	6	11	8	895	28 x 12	8 x 6	2 x 6	Apr 1804 BU
Franchise, 36	Fr	Rochefort, 1798	28 May 1803	143	0	119	8⅛	37	6¾	11	8	898	26 x 12	2 x 12, 10 x 24 carr	2 x 12, 4 x 18 carr	Nov 1815 BU
Clara, 36	Sp	Ferrol, 1784	5 Oct 1804	144	6	120	2⅜	38	8¼	11	8	958	26 x 12	10 x 32 carr	2 x 9, 2 x 32 carr	1807 receiving ship; 1815 sold
Psyche, 36 ex-32	Fr	Nantes, 1798	14 Feb 1805	138	6	117	0	36	10⅛	10	5	846	24 x 12	8 x 18 carr	2 x 6, 2 x 18 carr	1812 sold
Cuba, 36 ex-*Pomona*	Sp	Ferrol, 1794	23 Aug 1806	142	4	116	2	37	7	11	0	873	26 x 12	6 x 24 carr	2 x 6, 2 x 24 carr	1811 hulked; 3 Apr 1817 sold
Helder, 32 ex-*Guelderland*	Du	Amsterdam, 1803	19 May 1808	134	11½	107	9⅜	37	10½	12	2	852	26 x 12	10 x 32 carr	2 x 6, 2 x 32 carr	1813 receiving ship; 1817 BU

The table includes only those ships which saw service as cruisers in the Royal Navy. The 28s are confined to frigate-built ships of about 580 tons and over armed with at least 9pdr upper deck guns. Armament is as carried in British service; where recorded, as captured armament is given in the line below. Later armaments, where known, are given in Table 45.

Notes:

[1] Originally rated as a 34 and intended to be armed with 24 x 9pdrs, 8 x 4pdrs + 4 x 12pdr carronades, 2 x 4pdrs + 2 x 12pdr carronades.

[2] Later rated as a 28-gun Sixth Rate.

[3] Later carried 12 x 32pdr carronades on quarterdeck and 2 x 12pdr + 4 x 32pdr carronades on forecastle.

Part II: The Ships

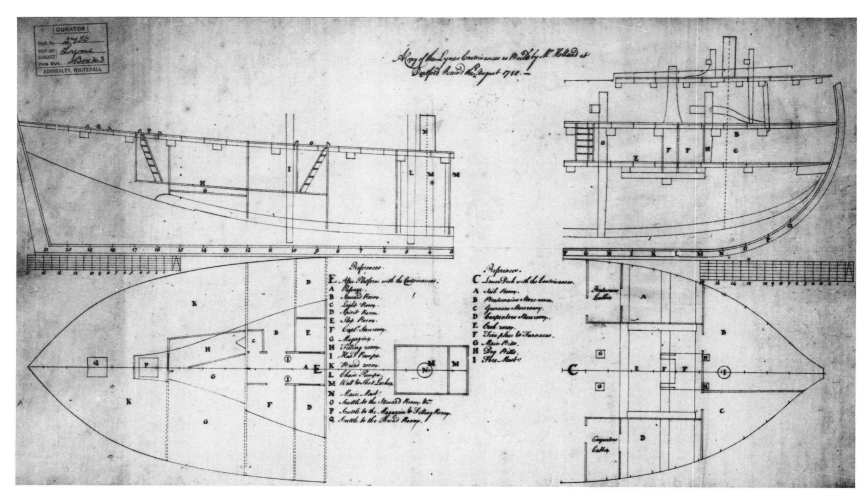

Lyme of 1748, 'contrivances' (fittings on lower deck and platform) as built, dated 2 August 1748.

The novelty of the new frigate type meant a number of changes to the traditional internal arrangements of British ships, and the first two ships were to exert an important influence on all 28-gun ships thereafter. Because they were much deeper aft than forward, there was no room for a platform under the lower deck forward (there was only a 'coal hole' for the galley furnace fuel) so the magazine had to be sited aft; all the cabins, apart from the captain's, were on the lower deck, the boatswain's and carpenter's being forward next to their storerooms.

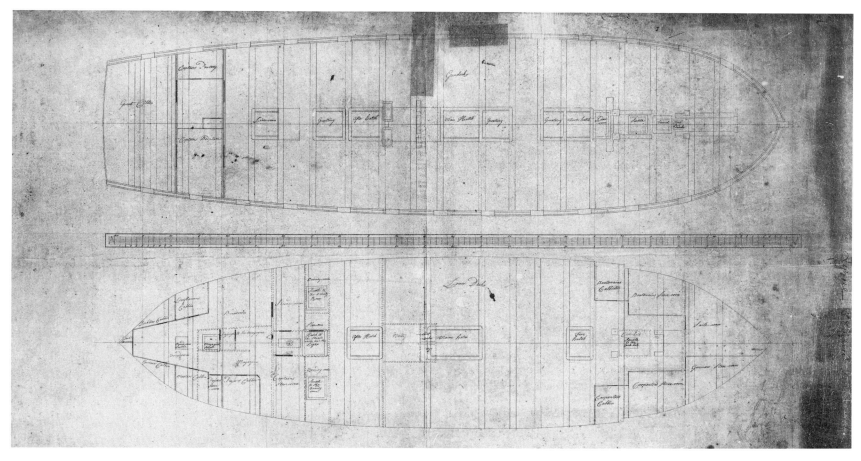

7. *Internal Arrangements and Fittings*

Lyme of 1748, upper deck and lower deck plans, undated but after completion.

The arrangements forward are similar to the as fitted 'contrivances' draught, except that the cabin partitions have been altered and the sailroom and boatswain's store have changed places; aft there are cabins for the lieutenant and 'doctor' (portside) and purser, master and gunner (starboard). The platform arrangements indicated in ticked lines seem to be the same as for the 'contrivances' draught.

A half-century of rigid but neat divisions between rates came to an end with the introduction of the frigate. Not only were the 28s, 32s and 36s entirely new classes – though they had seventeenth-century precedents – but being very large ships for their gun-power, the old Establishment proportions could not be used for any aspect of their fitting out, from masting to manning. However, less agile minds in the dockyards took some time to grasp the logic of the new design and the early ships suffered from difficulties which can only be explained by deeply entrenched habits of thought.

The biggest challenge was posed by the novelty of a completely clear lower deck (tradition was so strong that it continued to be called the 'gundeck', though totally unarmed, in many official lists until at least the 1790s.[36]) The original French concept, as expounded by Blaise Ollivier, was for a very lightly built deck of restricted headroom, which kept the height of topside to a minimum. Although the low 'tween deck was very common on merchant ships, the Royal Navy never fully espoused this approach, and seems to have regarded the new ships as something of a return to the old-style 20-gun ship of 1719 which had a properly framed full-height lower deck, even if it carried no guns. These ships had been fitted to row and to work their cables on the lower deck, and it is significant that the first all-British frigates, the *Southampton*, *Richmond* and *Pallas* classes, were all so fitted.

The *Unicorn* and *Lyme* were different because they had been ordered to be exact copies of their French privateer prototype and had the same low headroom between decks that, for example, made it impossible to man a capstan effectively. However, the succeeding pair, *Tartar* and *Lowestoffe*, had about 1ft added to the 4ft 'tween deck working headroom and this became the norm for later ships; the official reasoning emphasised 'such alterations as may tend to the better accommodation of men and carrying of guns'. The crew were berthed on the lower deck

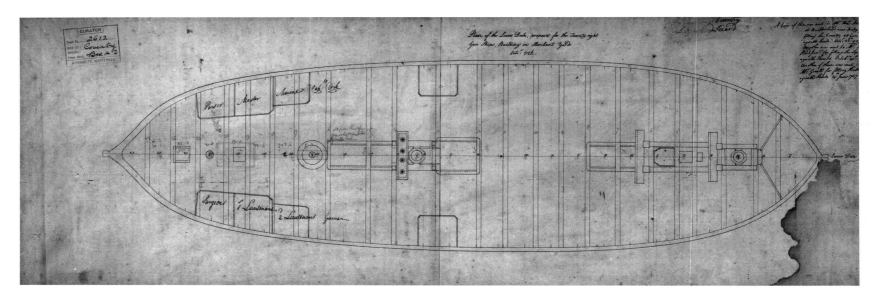

Coventry of 1757, design lower deck plan.

This group introduced a fore platform to which various storerooms and the sail room were transferred (necessary if the hawseholes were to be brought in on the lower deck) and the boatswain's and carpenter's cabins were moved amidships. By this time there was need to house a second lieutenant and a marine officer, while there are indications that cabins were to be added for the gunner and captain's clerk. The magazine remained aft and the fore platform arrangement was retained even after cable-handling was transferred to the upper deck.

and would benefit from the greater headroom, while as a result the upper deck would be raised further from the water, so the modification displayed the traditional British concern for habitability (they were high-endurance cruising ships) and fighting qualities (the increased

freeboard of the main battery allowed the ship to open her gunports in heavier weather). The layout of *Tartar* and *Lowestoffe* had followed the prototypes, but the draughts make it clear that the *Coventry* group was originally designed for lower deck cable-handling, although they reverted to the earlier pattern from *Maidstone* onwards and all the 28s

Boston of 1762, deck plans, undated but in the same style as the sheer & profile, so possibly a design set.

The 32s had enough depth in hold forward to allow the traditional British preference for a magazine forward, with a 'hanging' filling room below the level of the platform and forward of it. The surgeon and purser were allocated cabins on the after platform, the remaining officers being quartered on the lower deck, with the boatswain and carpenter separated amidships as in previous pre-frigate practice.

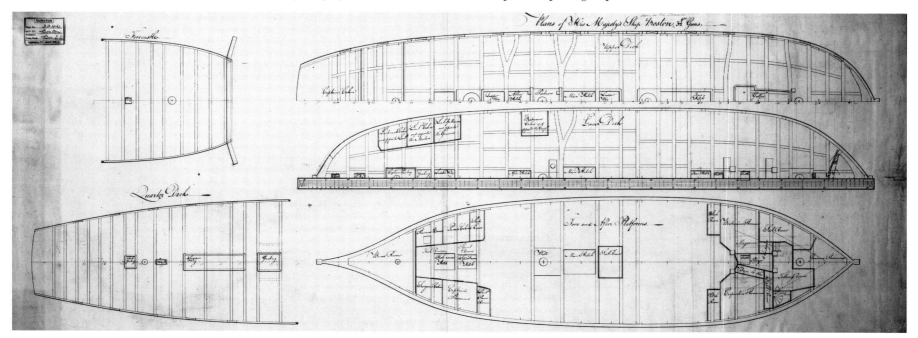

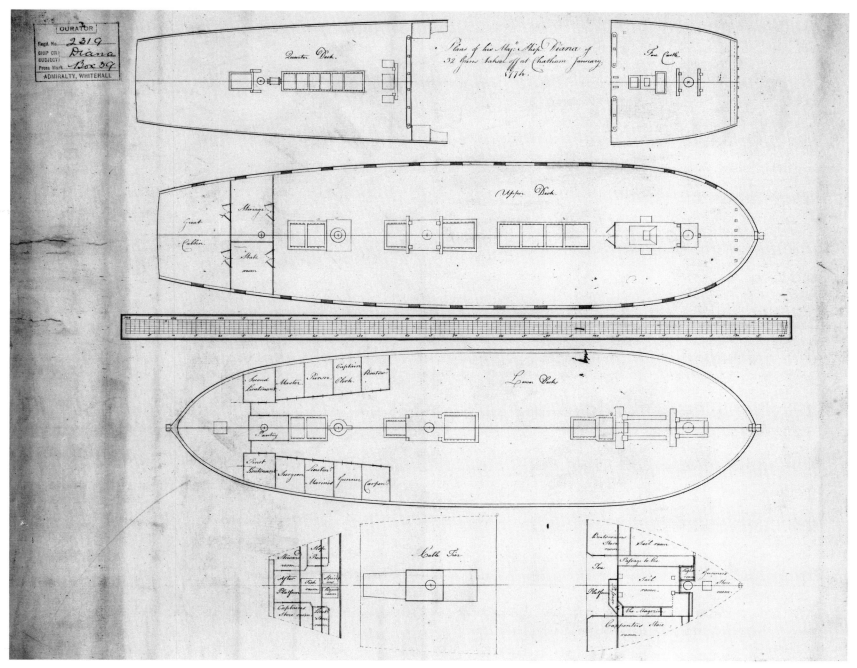

Diana **of 1757, deck plans, as taken off at Chatham, January 1774.**

The boatswain's and carpenter's cabins were eventually moved aft to join the others (it first occurs on the design deck plans of the *Brilliant* of 1757); this became the standard arrangement for 32s and was also adopted by the round-bow ships.

were soon refitted with capstans, bitts and hawseholes on the upper deck.

The first two pairs of 28s were completed with contrasting bow designs: *Unicorn* and *Lowestoffe* had traditional beakhead bulkheads while *Lyme* and *Tartar* had round bows.[37] In the *Unicorn*, bringing the cable in on the upper deck resulted in a very awkward arrangement of hawseholes that had to be positioned above the cheek pieces and below a false beakhead deck,[38] whereas the *Lyme*'s round bow presented no such difficulty. Thus it was probably the movement of cable-handling arrangements to the upper deck that signalled the end of the beakhead in single-battery ships. It was also unpopular with sea officers: in 1758 *Unicorn*'s captain complained of the 'interruption' it caused to her sailing when driving into a head sea and the Navy Board ordered the bow

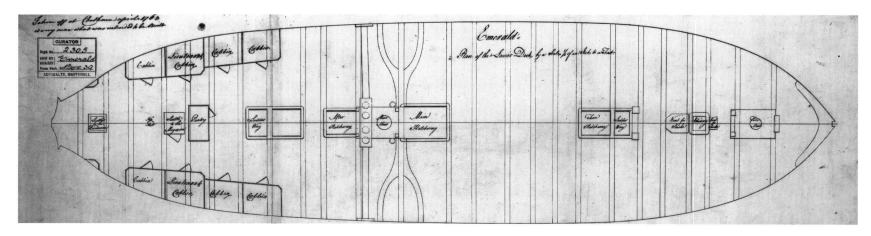

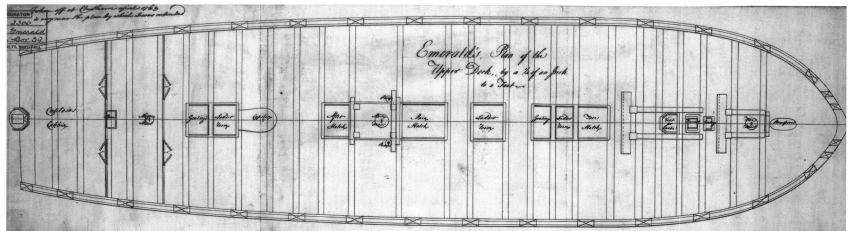

Emerald of 1763, as fitted upper and lower deck plans, taken off at Chatham, April 1763.

Annotated 'very near what was intended to be built', the design layout of these ships displays a few peculiarities: instead of being under the forecastle, the galley stove was on the fore platform, so the magazine had to be sited aft; the chain pumps also discharge on the lower deck, despite Slade's order to carry them up to the upper deck during construction. The stove was later moved to under the forecastle and an additional forward magazine and sailroom constructed on the platform, but this does not appear to have been carried out before the 1770s.

altered to the round pattern when it next required repair.[39]

The 32s and 36s had enough headroom to work their cables on the lower deck, but a fully rigged capstan required a lot of clear space that could have been used for cabins and storerooms, while the riding bitts took up further room forward; furthermore, the low position of the hawseholes would inevitably let in water at sea, which would have made life on the berth deck even more uncomfortable. To minimise this inadequacy, the *Richmond*s were given a sharp rise of deck forward in order to give the hawseholes more freeboard, a feature abandoned in the *Circe* class when the round bow and upper deck cable-handling were adopted.[40]

Apart from *Unicorn* and *Lyme*, the first generation of frigates also

had their chain pumps discharge on the lower deck where, it was quickly realised, the pumpdales were so near the waterline that the scuppers would not free the water at even moderate degrees of heel; they were promptly moved to the upper deck (the order to modify *Tartar* came a mere fortnight after the ship first went to sea).[41] In fairness, the Surveyors were quick to learn these lessons and the *Niger* and all subsequent classes had round bows and capstans, bitts and pumps on the upper deck.[42] The round bow occasioned one small problem in the fitting of the catheads, which had extended across the top of the beakhead bulkhead (the catbeam); fixing them on top of the deck was unsatisfactory because they would have interfered with the operation of the chase guns, so they were angled and secured under the forecastle deck beams (this novel feature warrants a separate sketch in some of the draughts of the period – the deck plan of *Alarm*, for example).

The only real advantage of a 'working' lower deck was the superior geometry it offered for rowing and the early 32-gun designs all show sweep ports on the lower deck, even the first draughts for the *Niger*s, which had an otherwise clear lower deck. In the event, they were moved to the upper deck in this class and the *Richmond*s,[43] but it is not clear whether the *Southampton*s made the change. The ability to use sweeps was taken very seriously by the Admiralty; although they were unpopular

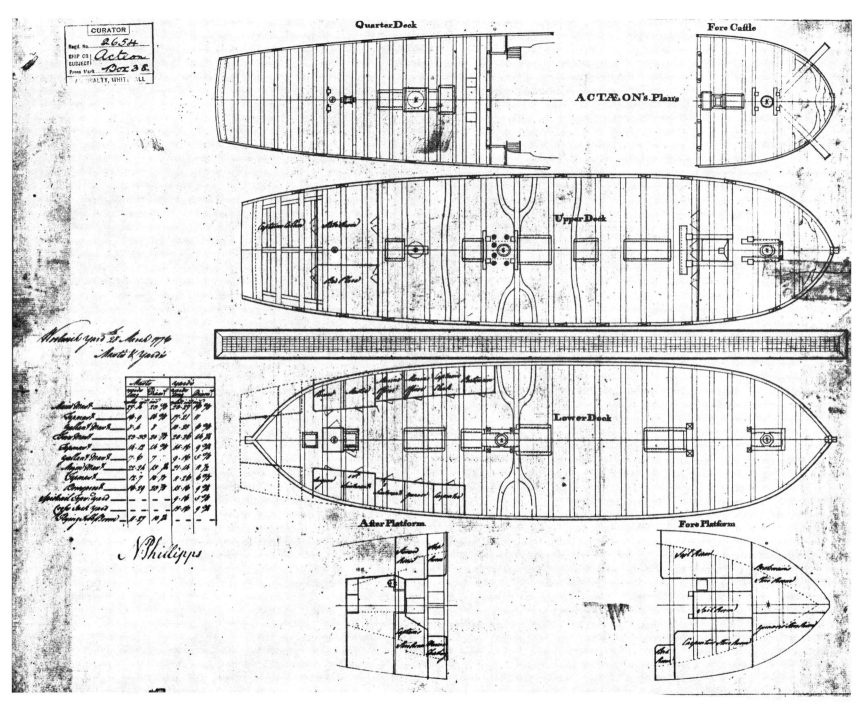

Actaeon of 1775, as fitted deck plans.

The final arrangement for the 28s, with the magazine retained aft, storerooms and sailroom on the forward platform (with only the coal storage below) and all the officers' cabins gathered together on the lower deck; the latter has now been increased to the number of eleven, by the addition of a second officer of the marines.

with some officers and often quietly abandoned in peacetime, in each war a standing order went out to see that frigates and sloops were so equipped, even if it meant cutting the necessary ports.[44] A similar order in 1777 led the Navy Board to protest that even 28s now carried their ports 7ft from the water so the efficacy of sweeps was doubtful, but as late as 1804 the *Circe* class draughts show sweep ports, which implies that they were of some utility.

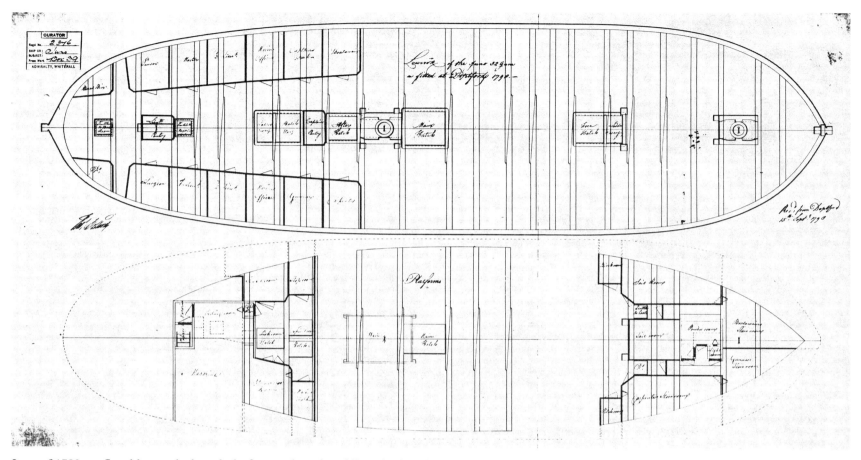

Juno of 1780, as fitted lower deck and platforms plan, dated Deptford 15 September 1798.

Later frigates had magazines both fore and aft, although this is not apparent from the design draughts of the *Amazon* class. Hunt's *Active*s of 1778 seem to be the first 32s to incorporate the extra magazine at design stage, but earlier surviving ships were retrofitted when convenient, as in this 1798 plan. On the lower deck the cabins are, from aft: (portside) purser, master, third lieutenant, marine officer, captain's clerk; (starboard) surgeon, first lieutenant, second lieutenant, marine officer, gunner, carpenter; the spaces right aft are 'bread bins'.

Niger class of 1757, design quarterdeck & forecastle plan.

This class introduced an extension of the quarterdeck called the 'fixed part of the gangway'; the gangways themselves were still very narrow, although this drawing shows a later amendment increasing their width.

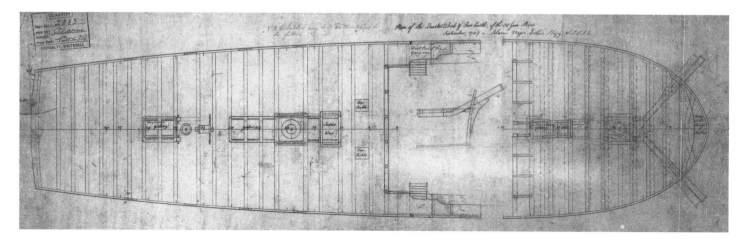

Table 40: BOAT ESTABLISHMENTS 1755-1790

Date	Boat	36-gun ships	32-gun ships	28-gun ships
15 Apr 1755	Longboat-yawl[1]			
	Pinnace			one 30ft
As comp 1756	Longboat	one 23ft (light)	one 23ft (light)	one 22ft
	Pinnace	one 30ft	one 30ft	one 28ft
	Yawl[2]	one 24ft	one 24ft	
19 Aug 1757	Deal cutter			one 24ft[3]
14 Dec 1761	Longboat	one 23ft	one 23ft	one 22ft
	Pinnace	one 30ft	one 30ft	one 28ft
	Yawl	one 24ft	one 24ft	one 22ft
18 Jul 1769	Longboat	one 23ft	one 23ft	one 22ft
	Pinnace	one 30ft	one 30ft	one 28ft
	Yawl[4]	one 24ft	one 24ft	one 23ft
12 Jul 1780	Longboat	one 23ft		
	Pinnace	one 30ft		
	Cutters	two 24ft		
19 Oct 1780	Launches ordered to replace longboats in all single-deck ships [*ie* those of 38-20 guns]			
14 Jun 1781	A 4-oared 18ft cutter added for all Rates			
1781	Launch	one 23ft or 24ft	one 23ft or 24ft	one 22ft
	Pinnace	one 30ft	one 30ft	one 28ft
	Cutters	two 24ft	two 24ft	[5]
		one 18ft	one 18ft	one 18ft
1 Aug 1783	A barge to replace the pinnace in 36s and 36s			
12 Jan 1784				30ft pinnace to replace 28ft boat

Notes:

[1] This term apparently described a short longboat that may have been clinker-built; it is unclear if this establishment for Sixth Rates of 20 guns was applied to the new 28s.

[2] Described as a 'Deal cutter' in a Navy Board letter of 19 Jun 1765.

[3] All Sixth Rates on Channel Service ordered to replace 10-oared boat [pinnace] with a more seaworthy 6-oared Deal cutter.

[4] Cutter-built (*ie* clinker) for ships on Channel Service, carvel for those on Foreign Service, where maintenance was more problematical.

[5] Probably carried a cutter of 24ft length, but not actually specified.

Table 41: ANCHOR AND CABLE ESTABLISHMENTS *c*1780

	32-Gun Ships		28-Gun Ships	
	Number	Weight (Cwt-Qrs-Lb)	Number	Weight (Cwt-Qrs-Lb)
ANCHORS				
Bower	4	33-0-0	4	31-0-0
Stream	1	8-1-0	1	8-0-0
Kedge	1	4-0-0	1	4-0-0
	Number	Length in fathoms @ circumf in inches	Number	Length in fathoms @ circumf in inches
CABLES				
	7	100 @ 16½	6	100 @ 16
	1	100 @ 9½	1	100 @ 9
Viol	1	44 @ 10	1	42 @ 9½
Messenger	1	44 @ 10	1	44 @ 9½

From Admiral Rotheram's MS memoranda book (NMM SPB/15). The 36-gun data given in this book relate to the larger 18pdr class, so have been omitted.

of men from one end of the ship to another, which might be crucial in boarding situations; not surprisingly, the tendency towards wider gangboards became irresistible. Eventually, in 1782 gangways were ordered to be built flush with forecastle and quarterdeck, and the waist gunwale raised, making the gangways a structurally permanent bridge between the two decks.[46] This ultimate development is best demonstrated in the draught of the *Hind*, the last 28 built to the lines of the *Unicorn*; in contrast to the separate decks of the prototype, the final ship displays broad, flush gangways radiused into the break of the quarterdeck.

One further advantage of more substantial gangways was the support they provided for the transverse skid beams on which the boats came to be stowed. Before the advent of gangways, the stowage of boats on small craft was always a problem, the alternatives being carriage on deck where they encumbered the guns, fore-and-aft stowage on the spare spars (probably only effective for one boat), or towing astern where they were vulnerable to loss.[47] For frigates, the provision and stowage of boats was even more important than for larger ships: the upper deck battery was their main armament, so should not be even temporarily disabled; many of their duties, such as close blockade and the searching of neutrals, required a lot of boat work and the number of established boats was steadily increased; and, as cruisers, they could not accept the additional drag of boats towed astern.

The official number, type and size of frigate's boats are given in Table 40, but the reality was more complicated, especially in wartime. It is not clear what boats *Unicorn* and *Lyme* first took to sea, although they probably carried a pinnace and a yawl – possibly a 'longboat-yawl' as the short longboat seems to have been termed; even the 1755 boat Establishment quoted in the table suggests all Sixth Rates (conventionally listed as '20-gun ships') had the same boats, whereas a Navy

Another alteration was the gradual process of integrating the forecastle and quarterdeck with wider, more permanent and eventually flush-planked gangways. As built, *Unicorn* and *Lyme* had entirely separate decks fore and aft, but thereafter the 28s were given narrow gangways (during fitting out, *Tartar* was ordered to have gangways constructed and her booms raised, and this set the precedent for succeeding ships).[45] The gangboards were still narrow and removable, but the quarterdeck proper was then given a short extension on either side which is sometimes delineated on draughts as 'the fixed part of the gangway'. In wartime the advantages of substantial gangways included the ability to fit swivel stocks along the waist without interfering with the main armament as well as allowing the rapid transfer of large bodies

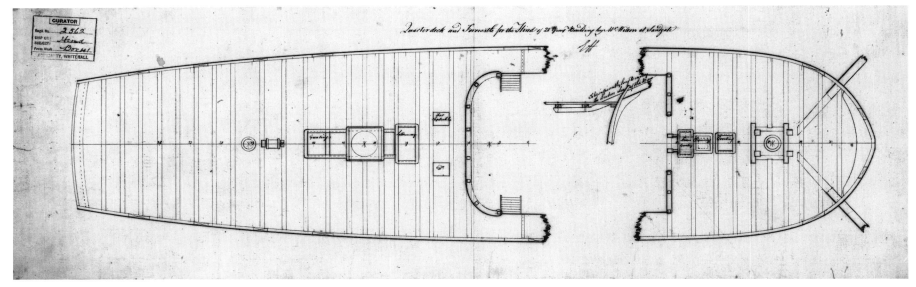

Board letter of 1765 says that 28s first carried a 22ft longboat and a 28ft 8-oared pinnace, 'to which a 24ft cutter has since been added.'[48]

This last addition came about because of the representations of the *Coventry*'s captain, who claimed that neither of his boats could board a ship at sea. It was obviously common for captains to replace the expensive Establishment craft whenever fancy and opportunity coincided, so the Navy Board proposed the substitution of the light clinker-built Deal cutter for the less seaworthy pinnace and this was duly ordered for all Sixth Rates on Channel service.[49] While undoubtedly better seaboats, cutters were poorer rowing craft and being somewhat fragile were difficult and expensive to maintain. This made them unpopular with the Navy Board who continued to prefer yawls, and when a 22ft boat was added to the 28s' Establishment in 1761 it was specified as a yawl.

The longboat, which was the heavy-duty harbour workboat, was not a lot of use to a cruising frigate at sea and ships on the Channel station

Hind of 1785, design quarterdeck & forecastle plan.

This late 28 demonstrates the effect of the order of 1782 raising the waist and making the gangway flush; the gangways are still relatively narrow, however. The sketch shows the run of the catheads under the forecastle.

Lowestoffe of 1761, contemporary model (facing page).

This finely detailed model includes the ship's pinnace carried on the spare topmasts amidships in the original manner, but does not indicate how the longboat and the yawl were stowed. This underlines the problem of boat stowage for frigates before substantial transverse skid beams were introduced - it is hardly surprising that frigate captains on Channel service liked to leave their longboats in harbour when cruising.

Circe class of 1804, design quarterdeck & forecastle plan.

Despite the order of 1782, the Surveyors had to be constantly reminded about making the gangways flush, most of the initial design draughts showing this as an alteration. This draught still indicates a separate gangway, although the sheer suggests it was changed during construction.

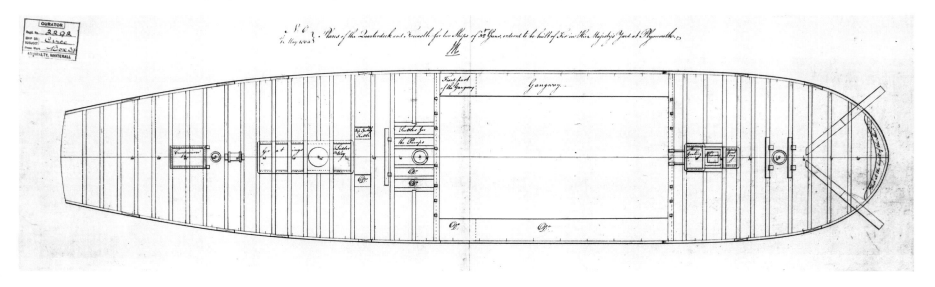

often left them behind or replaced them with lighter craft. By the end of the Seven Years' War, few frigates carried their official complement of boats, and Lord Colvill, the admiral commanding on the North America station, wrote to the Admiralty about the problem and proposed changes that might better suit the conflicting desires of the sea officers and the Navy Board.[50] He did not care for the longboat-yawls some of his frigates carried (they were an old-fashioned compromise type and all were 'heavy rowers') and proposed a slightly larger 24ft x 8ft longboat but, significantly, 'flat like a launch for stowing under the booms'. He also suggested a shorter (28ft) pinnace, 'a neat 4-oared yawl to be built after the manner of the pinnace [ie carvel-built]', and an additional cutter to every frigate that could stow one. The Navy Board's response was to deprecate all departures from the Establishment, and particularly the replacement of 'longboat-yawls' by cutters in ships on cruising stations, but it made the sensible point that it was impossible to supply special boats for particular services and that every type should be a compromise all-rounder suited to the nature of the ship that carried them: frigates, for example, carried a lot of topside weight on fine-lined hulls and so should not carry a large longboat.[51]

When the boat Establishment was next modified, in 1769, Colvill's recommendations were ignored, except in so far as the small yawl was allowed to be clinker-built like a cutter for ships on Channel service. However, his proposals were remarkably prescient, since during the next war the flatter launch (derived from a dockyard working craft) replaced the longboat, and cutters took over from yawls, while a small 4-oared cutter was added to the complement.

Richmond class of 1757, contemporary model.

Being intended for display, models tend to exhibit a higher degree of decoration than was expended on the prototypes, but while there is not much evidence for the painted stands of arms along the topsides, there is plenty to suggest that the bow and stern received as much attention from the carvers as the models indicate. This model has the low rails preferred in peacetime, but a series of hammock netting cranes along the quarterdeck show how additional protection was provided.

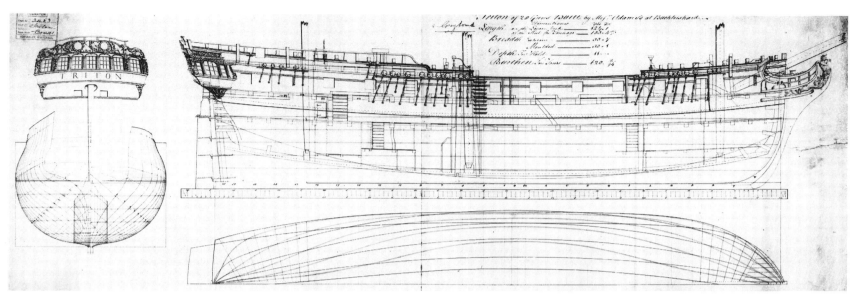

8. Appearance and Modifications

While the subject of appearance is more easily illustrated than described, a few generalisations are offered in this chapter to direct the reader's attention to specific aspects of the accompanying draughts. The typical sheer plan is a design tool and is not very helpful for details of decoration and finishing, but thanks to an Admiralty order of 21 September 1773 requiring 'as fitted' draughts of all new ships to be lodged with the Navy Board, one generation of decorative work is well represented (unfortunately, the practice was abandoned towards the end of the American War). However, most prizes are represented 'as taken' and provide an instant comparison with British practice, occasionally sharpened by the existence of an 'as refitted' plan showing exactly Royal Navy preferences.

The most visible changes to British frigates during this period affected the topsides, rails and bulwarks. In peacetime quarterdeck rails tended to be light, open and low, while those on the forecastle were almost non-existent. Some protection for the waist and quarterdeck was afforded by hammock netting and weather cloths. During the Seven Years War, the after rails were usually raised to the level of the swivel stocks, but an order of 1760 suggests that they were often unofficially heightened and made solid ('berthed up' as it was termed) to the point where it was difficult to fire small arms over them (frigates so equipped were also deemed poorer sailers in consequence).[52]

During the American War, the introduction of the carronade led to the permanent berthing-up of the quarterdeck barricades, but, curiously, the forecastle was left unprotected, despite the fact that two carronades were allocated to this deck right from the first Establishment of 1779. However, during the next war the forecastle also acquired solid bulwarks, and the *Circe* class of 1804 were designed with them, their

Triton of 1773, as fitted design & profile draught.

The as fitted draughts of the 1770s provide rare detail on the decorative schemes of British ships of the period (this example can be compared with the design draught of *Mermaid* in Chapter 4). The figure is a well moulded triton blowing a conch, the tail being carried down the trailboard; the drifts are square architectural hances in the French style; but most of the decorative effort is reserved for the taffrail, quarter pieces and the upper and lower finishing of the galleries. An order of 1770 introduced the painting of names on the upper counter and it is here depicted in the delicate serif type-style adopted for the ships of this generation.

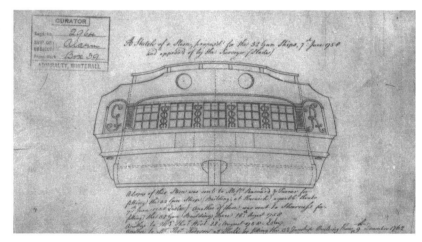

Niger class of 1757, sketch of stern.

Official drawings of decoration are almost unknown for British ships of this period, but occasionally a sketch like this will throw some light on what was intended. The quarter gallery lights are 'blind' and bear the GR monogram of the King, while the munnions between the lights are decorated with a caduceus motif (the herald's staff carried by Mercury – not inappropriate for a ship whose role included reconnaissance).

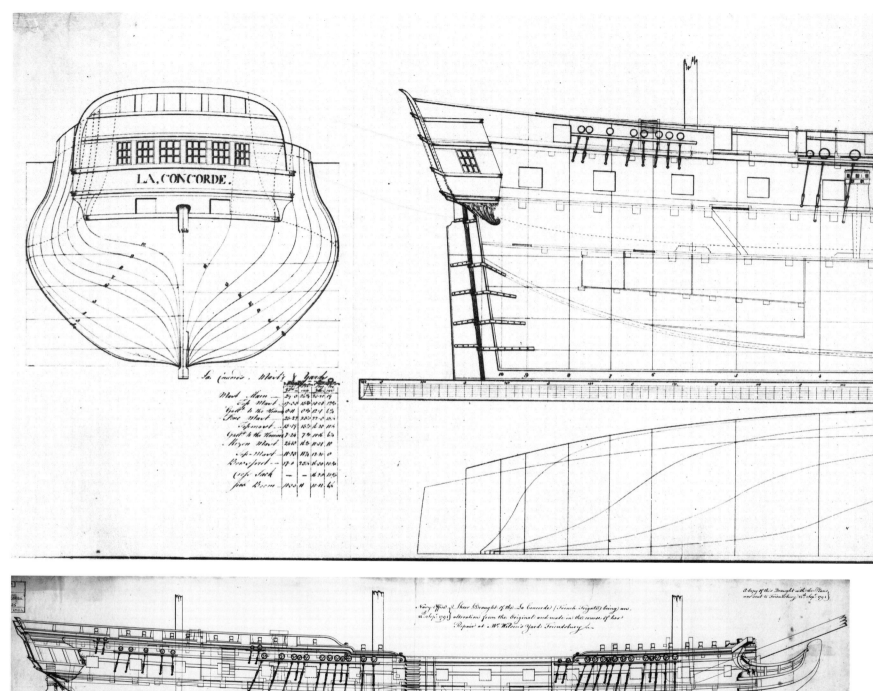

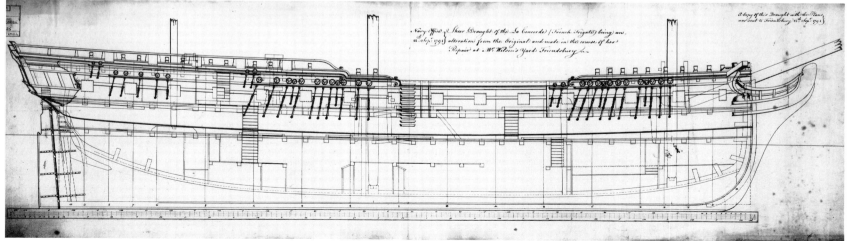

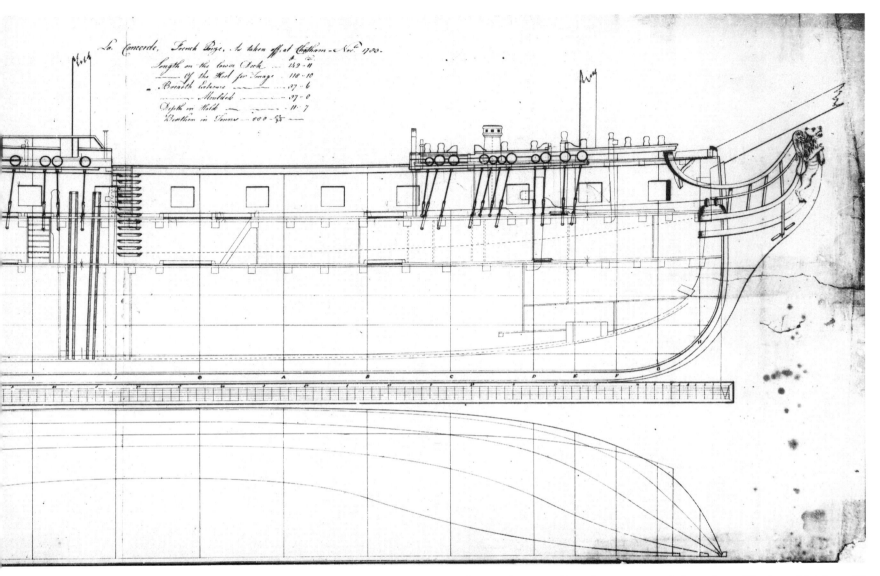

Concorde, sheer & profile draught for a major repair, dated 12 September 1791 (left).

Captured ships were usually subject to careful survey and a draught was then drawn up. When refitting French prizes for sea during wartime the minimal changes were usually made, subject to the findings of the survey, but occasionally the opportunity arose for major work. One such occasion was a threatened war with Spain in 1791, when a number of frigates were given extensive refits. *Concorde* was reconstructed at Wilson's Frindsbury yard, emerging with little to betray the ship's French origins. A study of the 'before' and 'after' draughts better reveals the differences between British and French aesthetics than a chapter of description.

Concorde, 32, ex-French, as captured sheer & profile draught taken off at Chatham, November 1783 (above).

Amazon class of 1770, contemporary model.

The stylistic features of British frigates – indeed all Royal Navy warships – did not alter dramatically between 1750 and 1790. The hull showed more sheer than French ships and there was always careful attention paid to the fairing in of the lines of the head and the quarter gallery; even after bulwarks were berthed up, the elegant plansheer line that had represented the top of the rails continued to be revealed as a moulding. The war austerity look of the late 1790s reduced decoration but the simple elegance of the lines remained.

draughts forming an interesting comparison with the *Richmond*s of fifty years earlier. There were subtler changes, including the general reduction in sheer, and a lighter head.

Between the 1750s and 1790s decorative schemes did not change dramatically. From as early as *Unicorn* most frigates had individual figureheads but they were sometimes replaced with plain billet or scroll heads if damaged in wartime, and the ships built after 1793 adopted this austerity measure from completion. Quarter galleries usually contained three equal sized windows, or 'lights' (the *Unicorn* and the three *Mermaid*s seem to be the only exception, having two), but some of Slade's later ships (*Lowestoffe* and the later *Mermaid*s) had a far larger, round-headed centre light, which also occurred on the *Lyme*. The elaborate decoration depicted on the topsides of Navy Board models is unlikely to reflect full size practice, but the 'as completed' draughts of the 1770s and 1780s do suggest that the stern, quarter galleries and head (the trailboard in particular) received surprisingly detailed

Brune, 32, ex-French, as captured sheer & profile, taken off at Plymouth March 1761.

Because French ships continued to be designed in the dockyards, they were more varied in appearance than their British equivalents. However, there were consistent features, such as the very architectural style of the stern and quarter galleries, relatively flat sheer, and exaggerated tumblehome (see Chapter 1 for earlier examples). Some had small poop cabins – usually promptly removed in British service – and different internal arrangements (a capstan on the forecastle was one visible difference). Stem profiles varied but *Brune*'s backward radiused form was common in the mid-century, although a plumb upright one became popular later. Stylistic quirks like square drifts (hances) also marked out French ships.

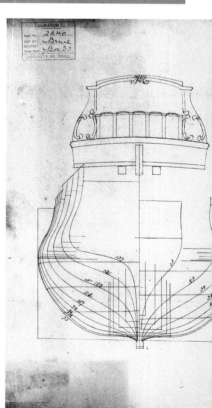

carving.[53] Names were painted 'as large as possible' on the upper counter from 1772.[54]

Not much can be said with authority about the painting of frigates at this time, but some of the more accurate marine paintings of the period do show coloured grounds to the carved work of the bow and stern, as well as above the waist- or sheer-rail on the broadside. During the American War a few official orders suggest new restrictions on variety: in 1777 it was instructed that ships' sides were to be payed with a mixture of Stockholm tar and either red or yellow ochre; black varnish was to replace tar for mastheads and yards in 1779; from 1780 all new ships were to have their sides and yards painted either yellow or black according to the captain's wishes; from 1782 hammock cloths were to be painted on one side only.[55] As an example of a colour scheme of the period, *Minerva*, the first of the new 38s, was to be finished with 'three yellow lines above the wale'.[56]

The appearance of foreign frigates was distinctly different, making them instantly recognizable to a seaman's eye. French ships had a much flatter sheer, more nearly upright stem- and sternposts, and a far more 'architectural' style of galleries which did not blend with the sheer lines of the hull as smoothly as the British approach. This also applied to the head rails, and although the round bow was characteristic of French frigates from the first, the forecastle rails or bulwarks were not carried forward of the catheads but were sometimes joined by a straight bulkhead. Forecastle and quarterdeck rails normally terminated in a square hance; this might be enlivened by a carved supporter, but was

more often a plain cut-off. The topsides usually exhibited extreme tumblehome and in early ships this meant that the channels were placed below the gunports where the hull was broad enough to give lateral support to the masts. The architectural style of galleries disappeared in the 1760s to be replaced by a more British appearance, although French galleries were less standardised, if generally rather shorter, than in British practice.

Spanish ships resembled French vessels rather than British, while in general American frigates were not radically different in external appearance from those of the mother country. Dutch ships, however, had a distinctively heavy appearance, principally the result of a rather short, high-sided hull, a deep head and a fulsome stem profile. In Royal Navy service the degree of modification to prizes would depend on the circumstances of capture. The bare minimum would be the removal of any poop or cabins on the quarterdeck,[57] the construction below decks of the cabins, storerooms, magazines and shot lockers that Royal Navy practice insisted upon, and the replacement of the small cook-places at the sides with a full sized hearth on the centreline. Other changes might involve the installation of chain pumps, double capstans (while removing the French forecastle capstan) and a reorganisation of the bitts. Structural strengthening was frequently needed, and if a major repair was called for, the ship might well emerge with British-style upperworks, quarter galleries and head. The extent of these radical changes can be seen in the 'before' and 'after' draughts of *Renown*, *Brune* and *Santa Margarita*, to give an example from each generation.

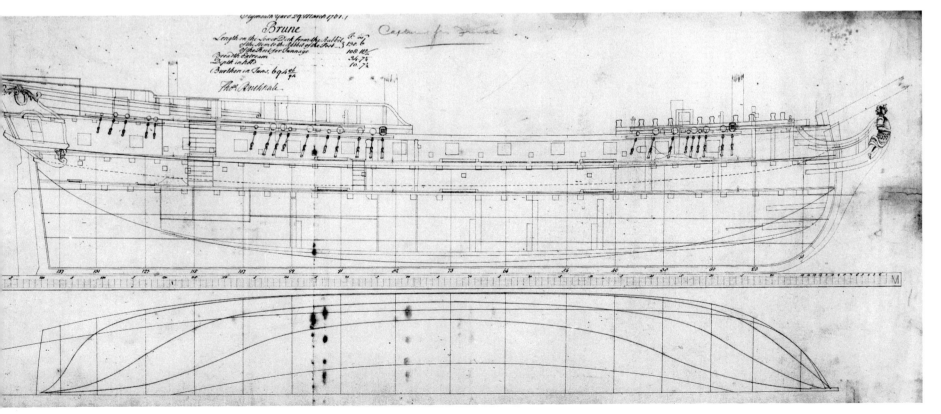

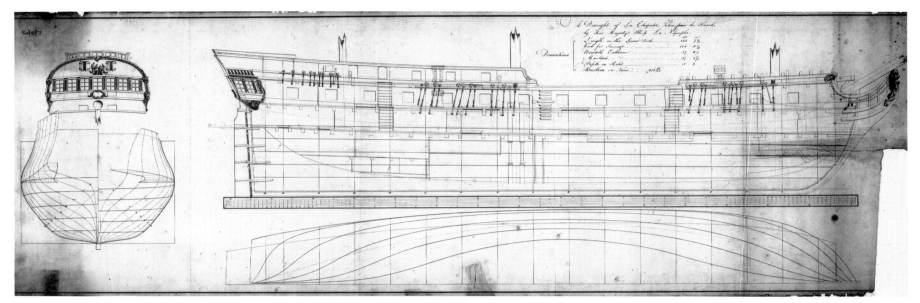

Table 42: SUMMARY OF MAJOR MODIFICATIONS AND APPEARANCE DIFFERENCES

Unicorn class, 28 guns

FIRST GROUP

As built: Unicorn had a beakhead and a unicorn figure; *Lyme* had a round bow and a standard lion figure.

Modifications: 23 Sep 1756: Guns added to quarterdeck, complement increased to 180 men (increased to 200, 22 Jun 1757).

SECOND GROUP

As built: Height between decks increased to 5ft; considerable internal rearrangements including moving boatswain's and carpenter's cabins from fore platform to lower deck amidships. Possibly intended to put hawseholes on lower deck originally but eventually brought in on upper by turning down the deck forward. *Tartar* had a round bow; *Lowestoffe* a beakhead.

Modifications: 9 Apr 1756: *Tartar* to have gangboards and booms raised.
17 May 1756: Both ships to have two chain pumps to work on upper deck.
8 Nov 1756: *Tartar*'s catheads to be altered.
28 Sep 1758: Scroll head to replace *Tartar*'s lion.

THIRD GROUP

As built: Sheer of quarterdeck reduced; wheel moved from abaft mizzen to before it and tiller (on the quarterdeck of early ships) brought in on lower deck. Further modifications to internal arrangements, including lower deck cable handling. However, only *Coventry*, *Lizard* and *Liverpool* were so completed, all later ships having hawseholes moved to upper deck (as did the first three when refitted – deck plans of *Coventry* dated Mar 1775 and *Liverpool*, July 1769, confirm the change). All ships had round bow. Fir-built ships had a square tuck stern and a different framing arrangement, with 'five tiers of futtocks'. *Levant* and *Carysfort* (and presumably the ships between them) had the first (spare) broadside gunport moved forward to a genuine chase position to replace the chase port inside the headrails of earlier ships. *Hind* had the topside appearance of the second generation ships, with a solid quarterdeck bulwark, and a breastrail curving into the fixed part of the gangways, which were flush and broader than in earlier ships.

Modifications: 30 Dec 1757: Fir ships to have their wales sheathed with elm boards amidships.
8 Nov 1758: *Aquilon*'s channels to be extended 2ft.
5 Jun 1759: All 28s to carry 50 instead of 40 tons of iron ballast.
4 Feb 1760: Fir frigates to carry 64 tons iron ballast.

Oiseau, 36, ex-French *Cléopâtre*, as captured sheer & profile draught, 1793.

From the 1760s French frigates began to adopt a more British style of quarter gallery. Gradually a new stern profile emerged, of approximately horseshoe shape, and although many *constructeurs* adopted it, the style has come to be associated with Jacques-Noel Sané, the finest ship designer of his generation. *Cleopâtre*, built by him at St Malo in 1781, demonstrates the new taffrail shape; the French were not so opposed to the beakhead bulkhead and went on using it occasionally until the end of the American Revolutionary War. The curiously shaped gunports on the quarterdeck are probably for *obusiers de vaisseau* (an early form of French carronade), although the ship did not mount any when captured.

Southampton class, 32 guns

As built: Lower deck lengthened by 3in during design. Cable handling and sweep ports on the lower deck; they do not seem to have been moved, deck plans for *Diana* dated 1774 and *Minerva* of 1770 showing the same arrangement.

Modifications: 31 May 1758: *Southampton*'s masts and spars to be increased (also 23 Aug which included *Diana*).

Richmond class, 32 guns

As built: Cable handling on the lower deck; they do not seem to have been moved, for a deck plan for *Lark* dated 1776 shows the same arrangement. Have sweep ports on upper deck and further ports on the lower; however, they are widely spaced and pass through cabins so are probably ventilation scuttles; there is what seems to be a ballast port amidships.

Modifications: 3 Jan 1758: *Juno*'s cable tier to be lengthened.

9 Apr 1759: *Thames* to have scuttles cut between decks, coamings raised, and 3in false keel added.

Niger class, 32 guns

As built: After the first four the draught was modified slightly with the rabbet of the stem moved a little further forward and the quarterdeck ports altered; from *Emerald* the steeve of the bowsprit was reduced. They were the first 32s designed with a fixed part of the gangway. Pumps moved to the upper deck during construction.

Modifications: 25 Apr 1761: Reduce steeve of bowsprit, extend main channels by one deadeye and add watering cock to *Niger*.
23 Oct 1761: *Alarm* to be copper-sheathed.

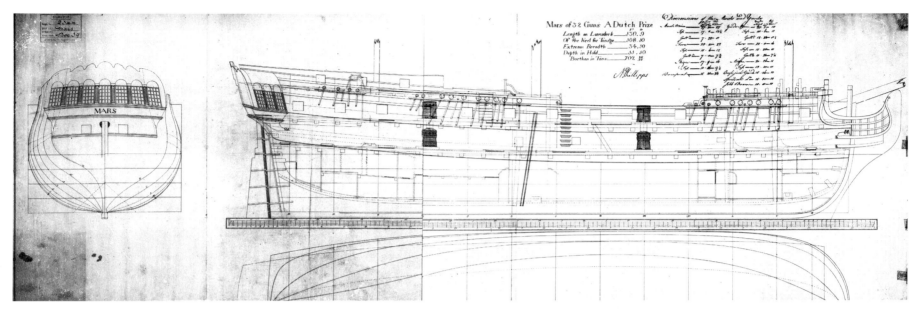

Mars, 32, ex-Dutch, as captured sheer & profile, 1781.

Dutch ship design in the eighteenth century tended to be very conservative, this frigate, for example, retaining a full height lower deck on which she worked her cables and a beakhead bulkhead. The relatively tall topsides and deep low head tends to make the ship look ungainly, and even frigates built in the 1790s (like the *Heldin*) continued to work their cables on the lower deck.

Santa Leocadia, 36, ex-Spanish, as captured sheer & profile taken off at Portsmouth, October 1781.

Spanish naval architecture was highly regarded in the late eighteenth century, having forged a native synthesis between the design principles of France and the robust construction of Britain. However, to achieve both required big ships, and Spanish warships were even larger than French for their gun-power. This ship was one of a fine class of frigates, four of which were captured by the Royal Navy; as big as a British 18pdr 38, some were armed with only 8pdrs when taken. In general, their decorative schemes and layout follows French practice more closely than British.

Tweed class, 32 guns

As built: Very probably had round bow; deck plan of 1769 shows upper deck cable handling.

Modifications: 8 May 1760: 'to receive her capstan on her main deck' (this may mean that it was originally on the lower deck).
31 Jan 1763: Capstan to work on the quarterdeck.

Pallas class, 36 guns

As built: No sweep ports shown on any draught.

Modifications: 28 Nov 1759: *Pallas* to carry 55 tons of iron ballast.
30 Jun 1762: *Brilliant*'s topmasts to be lengthened by 2ft.
9 Jun 1779: *Pallas* to have scuttles cut between decks.

Mermaid class, 28 guns

As built: Although retaining the *Mermaid*'s lines, *Hussar* and *Solebay* showed considerable alterations in the topside, principally an increase in the sheer ('made quicker') during the design stage (Feb 1762), which gave more freeboard fore and aft. In general, the second

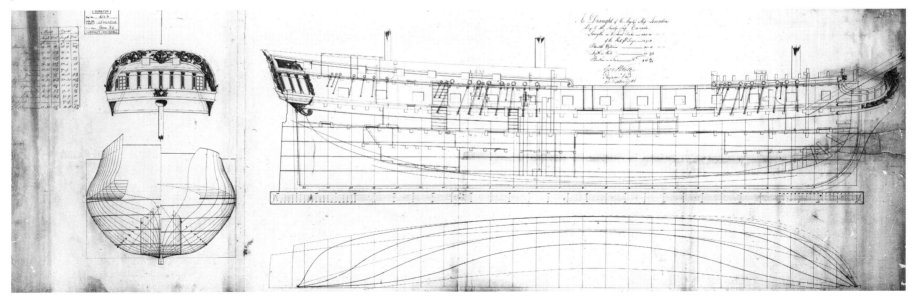

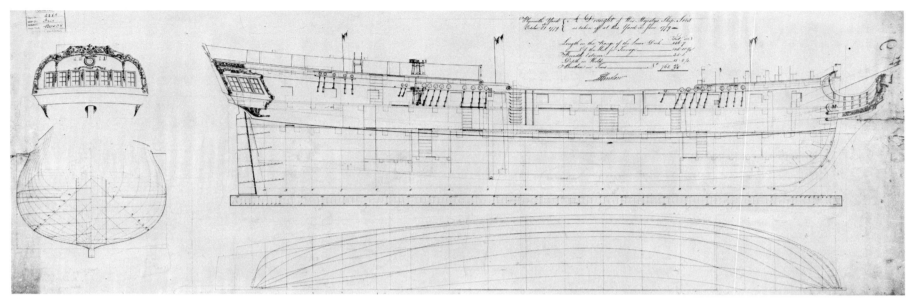

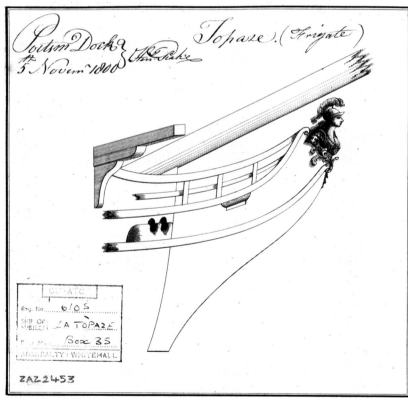

Iris, 32, ex-American *Hancock*, as captured sheer & profile, taken off.

Because there was no central naval administration, the appearance of early American frigates varied somewhat according to the whims of their various designers. In general, their decorative schemes were British rather than French in style, and for ships built so rapidly were surprisingly highly decorated; *Hancock* sported a figurehead portrait of John Hancock and a coiled rattlesnake motif on the taffrail with the motto 'Don't tread on me'.

Topaze, 38, ex-French, captured 1793; figurehead (?as repaired), Portsmouth Dockyard, November 1800

A rare draught depicting decorative work, this sketch shows the kind of bust which increasingly replaced the full figure as stem decoration from the 1790s.

out, producing a hull form closer to the *Mermaid*s'; like the *Lowestoffe*, officially, they are also described as 'nearly similar to the *Aurora* prize', but they might be regarded as a separate class.

Modifications: 17 Dec 1761: *Lowestoffe* to carry 10 tons more ballast.
26 Mar 1776: *Diamond* to be fitted with gangboards.

Razée 44-gun ships

As reconstructed: No draught survives for *Adventure*, but in outward appearance *Sapphire* resembled contemporary 32s, except that the disposition of ports allowed only a quarter badge rather than a complete gallery. The rudder head protruded on to the quarterdeck, but it is not clear where the tiller worked.

Enterprize class, 28 guns

As built: Unlike Slade, Williams was disinclined to modify his designs continuously and as a result alterations were minor and the product of wartime experience. The 1782 ships (*Hussar* onwards) had solid quarterdeck bulwarks and flush gangways.

Amazon class, 32 guns

As built: Like the *Enterprize*s, this class was not much modified; as completed, the later ships (from at least the *Amphion* onwards) had solid quarterdeck bulwarks with two large carronade ports a side, abaft the mizzen, with the mizzen channels and backstay stools altered accordingly. Both *Amazon* and *Ambuscade* were later fitted for carronades (by 1782).

Active class, 32 guns

As built: Head lengthened slightly during design; most of the class fitted for carronades so presumably had solid quarterdeck bulwarks (but as repaired in Mar 1792 *Daedalus* reverted to open rails and no carronade ports).

group were similar but there were further very small alterations to the profile of the bow and stern and the bowsprit was raised.

Modifications: 1 Oct 1778: *Hussar* to have oar ports cut.

Lowestoffe class, 32 guns

As built: *Lowestoffe* and *Mermaid* were designed simultaneously and exhibit the same French-style flat sheer and near plumb stem- and sternposts; as with the follow-on *Mermaid*s, the *Orpheus* and *Diamond* exhibit increased sheer and other topside alterations. However, the hull lines were also modified, the relatively sharp turns of bilge being rounded

Andromeda class, 32 guns

As built: Waist gunwale raised and gangways made flush during design; the first pair were designed with open quarterdeck rails with four gunports a side, but later ships had solid bulwarks extended to the main mast and six ports (numbers 3 and 6 from forward being carronade ports); this involved some modifications to the mizzen channels and backstay stools.

Heroine class, 32 guns

As built: After being purchased in frame, this ship was much modified in detail: gangways made flush and waist gunwale raised; forecastle lengthened; solid quarterdeck bulwark extended almost to main mast; oar ports cut; cross pieces to gallows bitts and hook under bowsprit added; while Navy standards were enforced in respect of many smaller fittings – tiller, hawseholes, riding bitts and hatchways are mentioned on the draught.

Shannon class, 32 guns

As built: Fitted out using the standard *Pallas* class profile draught but to a different framing arrangemnent, with the usual square tuck of fir-built ships; bulwarks fore and aft modified to accommodate carronades.

Triton class, 32 guns

As built: Fore mast moved forward about 4½ft (March 1797); rudder narrowed slightly in profile.

Circe class, 32 guns

As built: Compared with their *Richmond* class model, these ships had one less gunport a side, a square tuck stern, and were much modified forward (bringing the hawseholes in on the upper deck allowed the sharp rise of the decks to be reduced; the round bow was then combined with a flatter, shallower head); the position of the oar ports was adjusted slightly during design. All had solid bulwarks fore and aft, and the Plymouth ships were built to a marginally different framing scheme from the rest.

9. Armament

Because existing Sixth Rates were armed with 9pdrs, the introduction of the *Unicorn* type caused no difficulties to the Board of Ordnance, who continued to issue the standard 23½cwt, 7ft weapons. There is no doubt that the new ships were considered '24s', because they had a spare upper deck gunport that was left deliberately empty, in contrast to the much-criticised British habit of cramming extra guns into French prizes (in reality, many French privateers had their armament *reduced* in British service).

Captured French frigates, on the other hand, did cause some confusion to a rating system that was two generations old and consequently an ingrained habit of thought: the long quarterdecks of these ships

Amazon class of 1770, contemporary model.

Besides their rated armament, frigates carried a complement of ½pdr swivel guns (usually twelve in number). The stocks for these can be seen along the quarterdeck and forecastle of many draughts. The swivels could be shipped and unshipped as required so are not always depicted on models, although this one has some right aft on the quarterdeck and also on the forecastle; two of the swivels retain the tiller used for aiming. This model predates the introduction of the carronade and has the usual 32-gun ship's eight 6pdrs on the quarterdeck; the shot garlands are still sited along the rails.

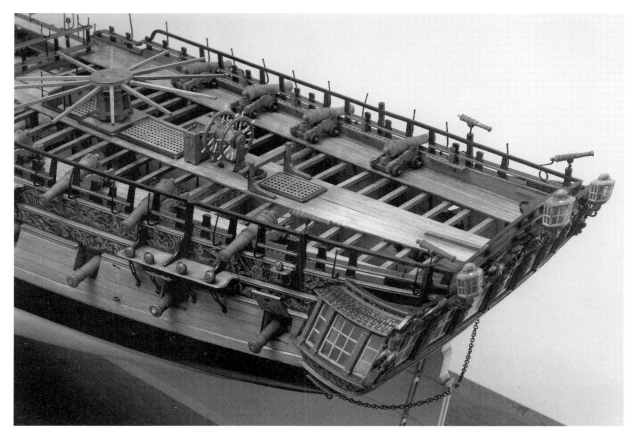

Table 43: MAXIMUM AMMUNITION ALLOWANCES c1770

| | | Foreign or (Channel) Service | | | |
| | | Type of ammunition | | | |
Rate	Calibre	Round shot		Grape	Double
28 guns	9pdr	2400	(1680)	288	72
	3 or 6pdr	400	(300)	48	
	½pdr	720	(600)	144	
32 guns	12pdr	2600	(1820)	260	78
	6pdr	600	(420)	60	
	½pdr	720	(600)	144	
36 guns	12pdr	2600	(1820)	182	78
	6pdr	1000	(700)	70	
	½pdr	720	(600)	144	

Reconstructed from information on specific ships in PRO Adm 95/66.

24pdr carronade, 'in the English fashion', Swedish official draught dated 31 December 1795.

Because British naval guns were provided by the Board of Ordnance and not the Navy Board, there are very few drawings of guns in the Admiralty Collection, and virtually no standard weapons. Abroad the new carronade received much attention and there are both Danish and Swedish drawings of British guns. This is the 24pdr carronade in its developed form, with a 'nozzle' (extension to the muzzle) and a screw elevating mechanism. This was the standard carronade for 12pdr frigates. *(Krigsarkivet, Stockholm)*

Réunion, 36, ex-French, as captured sheer & profile taken off at Portsmouth, January 1794.

By the 1790s the carronade began to be fitted in large numbers to the upperworks of British frigates. Because of the short length of the barrel, which did not extend far beyond the ship's side, the port had to be large to allow safe elevation, and at first they could not be positioned 'in the wake of the shrouds' where blast might damage the rigging. As a result, it is quite clear from the size of the gunport on draughts which weapon it was intended to house. France was slow to adopt the carronade and prizes often had their barricades altered to accommodate the new weapon - pencil alterations to this one indicate a carronade port right aft (the cabin on the quarterdeck would be removed) and one between the main and mizzen shrouds.

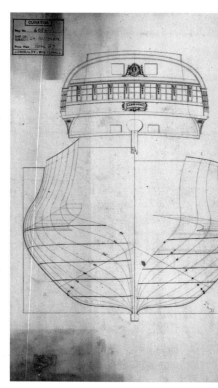

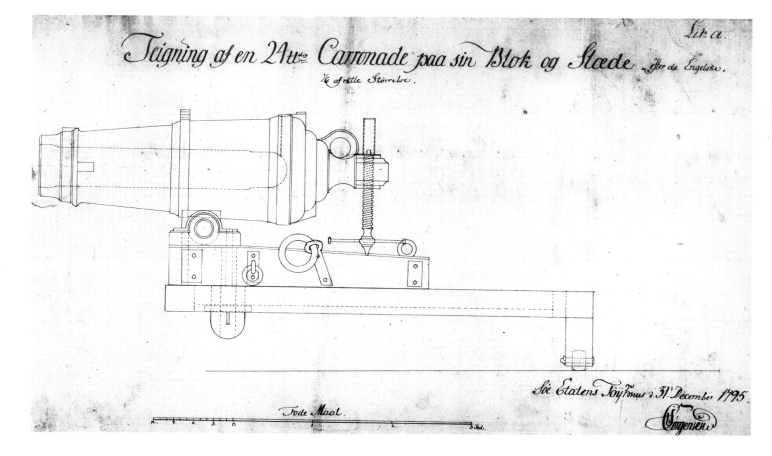

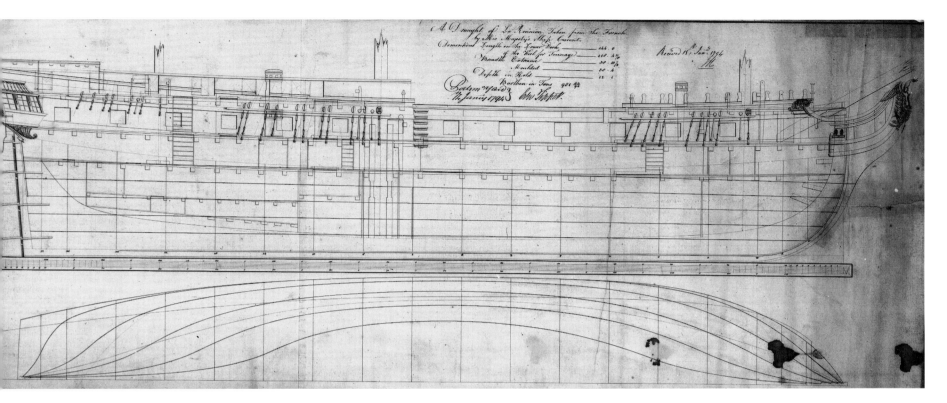

seemed to invite armament, but the Navy Board was uneasy with the resulting non-standard 30-gun rating. It was originally proposed, for example, to fit *Ranger*'s upperworks with only twenty swivels and give her the 160-man complement of an English 24, but eventually six 4pdrs replaced the swivels and the ship was to be manned with a more realistic 220 men. The Navy Board still needed direction as to whether 30-gun ships like *Bellona* and *Renown* were Fifth or Sixth Rates (settled by Admiralty directive on 22 April 1751 in favour of the latter), whereafter force of habit caused them to be listed as '24s'. (*Ambuscade* posed no problem because, despite only mounting 40 guns, she was treated as a standard 44.) The issue was further clouded from the mid-1750s by the introduction of a new smaller frigate-built 20-gun ship to supersede the old 24.

It is probable that if the war had still been in progress when they were completed *Unicorn* and *Lyme* would have carried some quarterdeck armament, because the principle was well established by 1748. The 1755 order for the second group certainly refer to them as ships 'of 28 guns by the draught of the *Lyme*' and on 22 September 1756 the earlier pair were ordered to carry 28 carriage guns and 180 men. The additional guns were 7¼cwt, 4½ft 3pdrs allocated to the quarterdeck.

Unlike the 28, the new 32- and 36-gun classes had no direct antecedents, and this was to cause some initial difficulties. Their main calibre, the 12pdr, was carried by nothing smaller than the 50-gun ships, and although the latest 8½ft model (the shortest available) was supplied to the first of the new frigates, it proved too long. Captain Gilchrist of the *Southampton* was the first to complain, in August 1757, and the

Board of Ordnance undertook to produce a special short gun within a year.[58] This 28½cwt, 7½ft weapon was matched with an equivalent short 6pdr (16½cwt, 6ft) for the quarterdeck. All frigates were gradually converted to the new weapon, including French prizes, so they were usually in short supply: *Tweed*, for example, jettisoned hers to escape a superior force and had to go to sea in 1760 with short 9pdrs in lieu.

The other increase to all frigates' armament from the outbreak of war in 1756 was the provision of twelve ½pdr swivel guns, allowed to all ships from 70 guns downwards. These anti-personnel weapons were mounted in iron crutches on fixed stocks along the rails, and draughts sometimes show four of the stocks a side on the quarterdeck and two on the forecastle; from about 1760, a fit of only six swivels seems to be more common. They were also mounted in the tops, but these of course are not obvious from the draughts.

Swivel stocks are to be found on new designs down to the middle of the War of American Independence, when they were rendered superfluous by the carronade, which was far more than an anti-personnel weapon and took up all the available topside space between the carriage guns. Although the 'berthed-up' solid bulwarks to the upperworks are usually associated with the introduction of the carronade, it is worth noting that an order of May 1760[59] instructed all frigates with quarterdeck 'barricades' to reduce them to a level that men could easily fire over with small arms. This development must have reflected unofficial enterprise by the captains concerned, but the carronade was to make solid bulwarks a necessity. The first official carronade Establishment was promulgated in August 1779 and by December complaints of muzzle flash were such that the Navy Board was instructing the Dockyards to make moveable barricades of old rope to prevent hammocks and lanyards to the shrouds catching fire – and so solid bulwarks may be more a question of blast protection than defence against enemy small arms' fire.[60] The elm boarding was ordered to be at least ½in thick, which would not be much protection against musketry, let alone grape shot.[61]

In February 1780 the 3pdrs on the quarterdecks of 28s and 24s were uprated to 6ft 6pdrs, but most of the concentration was on the obvious increases in firepower promised by the carronade. Some of the ramifications were arcane: shot racks were moved from the sides to the hatch coamings, partly to give more space to the new weapons, but largely to offset their weight. The carriages continued to give trouble and from March 1782 the slides were no longer made in the dockyards but were to be supplied with the carronades themselves by the Board of Ordnance.

Table 44: QUARTERDECK AND FORECASTLE ARMAMENT OF BRITISH 12pdr AND 9pdr FRIGATES, 1782-1815

Name	Date	Quarterdeck		Forecastle	
		Long guns	Carronades	Long guns	Carronades
Unicorn class, 28					
Lizard	22 Jul 1782	4 x 6pdr	2 x 18pdr		2 x 18pdr
Maidstone	22 Jul 1782	4 x 6pdr	4 x 18pdr		2 x 18pdr
Milford	22 Jul 1782	4 x 6pdr			2 x 18pdr
Carysfort	22 Jul 1782	4 x 6pdr	4 x 18pdr		2 x 18pdr
	c1808		2 x 18pdr	[24 x 32pdr carr UD]	
Hind	c1808	2 x 6pdr	6 x 24pdr		
Mermaid class, 28					
Triton	9 May 1793	4 x 6pdr	4 x 24pdr		2 x 24pdr
Enterprize class, 28					
Enterprize	22 Jul 1782	4 x 6pdr	4 x 18pdr		2 x 18pdr
Aurora	22 Jul 1782	4 x 6pdr	4 x 18pdr		2 x 18pdr
Proserpine	22 Jul 1782	4 x 6pdr	4 x 18pdr		
Sibyl	c1793		4 x 18pdr		2 x 4pdr
Nemesis	1 Apr 1793	4 x 6pdr	4 x 18pdr		2 x 18pdr
Mercury	22 Jul 1782	4 x 6pdr	4 x 18pdr		
	c1808	2 x 6pdr	4 x 18pdr	[24 x 32pdr carr UD]	
Pegasus	c1808		2 x 24pdr	[20 x 24pdr carr UD]	
Vestal	22 Jul 1782	4 x 6pdr	4 x 18pdr		
	c1808		4 x 18pdr	2 x 6pdr	2 x 18pdr
Hussar	1 Jan 1793	4 x 6pdr	4 x 18pdr		2 x 18pdr
Dido	23 Jun 1795	4 x 6pdr	4 x 18pdr		

Name	Date	Quarterdeck		Forecastle	
		Long guns	Carronades	Long guns	Carronades
Thisbe	As troopship	4 x 6pdr		2 x 9pdr	
				[14 x 32pdr carr UD]	
Lapwing	c1808	4 x 6pdr		[24 x 24pdr carr UD]	
Southampton class, 32					
Diana	22 Jul 1782	4 x 6pdr		2 x 6pdr	2 x 18pdr
Richmond class, 32					
Boston	22 Jul 1782	4 x 6pdr	4 x 18pdr	2 x 6pdr	2 x 18pdr
	31 Jul 1793	4 x 6pdr	4 x 12pdr	2 x 6pdr	2 x 12pdr
Jason	22 Jul 1782	4 x 6pdr	4 x 18pdr	2 x 6pdr	2 x 18pdr
Thames	24 Oct 1793	4 x 6pdr		2 x 6pdr	
	13 Aug 1796	4 x 6pdr	4 x 24pdr	2 x 6pdr	2 x 24pdr
	c1800		8 x 24pdr		4 x 24pdr
Niger class, 32					
Alarm	22 Jul 1782	4 x 6pdr	4 x 18pdr	2 x 6pdr	
	1 Jan 1793	4 x 6pdr	6 x 18pdr	2 x 6pdr	
Pearl	22 Jul 1782	4 x 6pdr	6 x 18pdr	2 x 6pdr	
Aeolus	22 Jul 1782	4 x 6pdr	4 x 18pdr	2 x 6pdr	2 x 18pdr
Apollo	22 Jul 1782	4 x 6pdr	4 x 18pdr	2 x 6pdr	2 x 18pdr
Stag	22 Jul 1782	4 x 6pdr	6 x 18pdr	2 x 6pdr	
Winchelsea	22 Jul 1782	4 x 6pdr	6 x 18pdr	2 x 6pdr	2 x 18pdr
Lowestoffe class, 32					
Diamond	22 Jul 1782	4 x 6pdr	4 x 18pdr	2 x 6pdr	2 x 18pdr
Lowestoffe	23 Jun 1797	4 x 6pdr	4 x 18pdr	2 x 6pdr	
Amazon class, 32					
Amazon	22 Jul 1782	4 x 6pdr	6 x 18pdr	2 x 6pdr	2 x 18pdr
Ambuscade	22 Jul 1782	4 x 6pdr	4 x 18pdr	2 x 6pdr	2 x 18pdr
	14 Dec 1798	4 x 6pdr	6 x 24pdr	2 x 6pdr	2 x 24pdr
Amphion	22 Jul 1782	4 x 6pdr	4 x 18pdr	2 x 6pdr	2 x 18pdr
	c1796		6 x 24pdr		6 x 24pdr
Orpheus	22 Jul 1782	4 x 6pdr	4 x 18pdr	2 x 6pdr	
Juno	22 Jul 1782	4 x 6pdr	2 x 18pdr	2 x 6pdr	
	1 Jan 1793	4 x 6pdr	4 x 18pdr	2 x 6pdr	
	31 Jan 1793	4 x 6pdr	4 x 18pdr	2 x 6pdr	2 x 18pdr
Success	c1808	2 x 6pdr	8 x 24pdr	2 x 6pdr	2 x 24pdr
Andromache	22 Jul 1782	4 x 6pdr	4 x 18pdr	2 x 6pdr	2 x 18pdr
	c1808		4 x 24pdr		2 x 24pdr
Solebay, ex-*Iris*	c1808		8 x 24pdr	2 x 6pdr	2 x 24pdr

Name	Date	Quarterdeck		Forecastle	
		Long guns	Carronades	Long guns	Carronades
Greyhound	*c*1808	4 x 6pdr		2 x 9pdr	2 x 18pdr
Castor	20 Dec 1793	?4 x 6pdr	4 x 24pdr	?2 x 6pdr	2 x 24pdr
	*c*1808	2 x 6pdr	4 x 32pdr	2 x 12pdr	2 x 32pdr
				[22 x 32pdr carr UD]	
Active class, 32					
Daedalus	22 Jul 1782	4 x 6pdr	6 x 18pdr	2 x 6pdr	2 x 18pdr
	*c*1808		8 x 24pdr	2 x 6pdr	2 x 24pdr
Mermaid	20 Feb 1793	4 x 6pdr	4 x 18pdr	2 x 6pdr	
	9 Feb 1799	4 x 6pdr	6 x 24pdr	2 x 6pdr	
Cerberus	22 Jul 1782	4 x 6pdr	6 x 18pdr	2 x 6pdr	2 x 18pdr
Active	22 Jul 1782	4 x 6pdr	4 x 18pdr	2 x 6pdr	2 x 18pdr
Fox	22 Jul 1782	4 x 6pdr	6 x 18pdr	2 x 6pdr	2 x 18pdr
Astraea	10 Apr 1795	4 x 6pdr		2 x 6pdr	
	*c*1808		4 x 24pdr	2 x 6pdr	2 x 24pdr
Quebec	*c*1808	4 x 9pdr	4 x 24pdr	2 x 9pdr	2 x 24pdr
Hermione class, 32					
Hermione	22 Sep 1797	4 x 6pdr	6 x 24pdr	2 x 6pdr	
Druid	*c*1808		8 x 24pdr	2 x 6pdr	2 x 24pdr
Blanche	1 Jan 1795	4 x 6pdr	4 x 18pdr	2 x 6pdr	2 x 18pdr
Heroine, 32	31 Jan 1793	4 x 6pdr	4 x 18pdr	2 x 6pdr	2 x 18pdr
Maidstone class, 32					
Maidstone	*c*1808		8 x 24pdr		4 x 24pdr
Pallas class, 36					
Venus	14 Feb 1793				
	[reduced to 32, 24 x 12pdr UD]				
		6 x 6pdr	4 x 18pdr	2 x 6pdr	2 x 18pdr

Notes:

The Progress Book for 1783-93 lists *Pearl* with 26 x 32pdr carronades on the upper deck, 4 & 2 x 18pdr carronades on quarterdeck and forecastle, but other evidence suggests this scheme was never carried out.

Amphion's Progress Book entry seems to indicate the usual long guns on the upperworks crossed out; *Castor*'s are also unclear.

The 6 carronades established in 1793 on *Triton*, *Nemesis*, *Juno* and *Heroine* were not allocated to quarterdeck or forecastle specifically.

The 1808-1816 list attributes no carronades to the following ships: 28s – *Alligator*, *Aurora*, *Brilliant*, *Cyclops*, *Dido*, *Enterprize*, *Medea* and *Nemesis*; 32s – *Alarm*, *Andromeda*, *Aquilon*, *Boston*, *Ceres*, *Cleopatra*, *Fox*, *Mermaid*, *Pearl*, *Southampton*, *Terpsichore* and *Winchelsea*.

Table 45: QUARTERDECK AND FORECASTLE ARMAMENT OF CAPTURED 12pdr AND 9pdr FRIGATES, 1778-1815

Name	Date	Quarterdeck		Forecastle	
		Long guns	Carronades	Long guns	Carronades
32-gun ships captured 1778-1783					
Aimable	*c*1808		6 x 24pdr	2 x 6pdr	
Concorde	20 Dec 1793	4 x 6pdr	4 x 24pdr	2 x 6pdr	2 x 24pdr
	23 Apr 1794	2 x 6pdr	6 x 24pdr	2 x 6pdr	4 x 24pdr
36-gun ships captured 1778-1783					
Prudente	30 Dec 1779	8 x 6pdr	6 x 18pdr	2 x 6pdr	2 x 18pdr
	9 Aug 1780	10 x 6pdr	4 x 18pdr	2 x 6pdr	2 x 18pdr
Santa Monica	8 Jan 1780	8 x 6pdr	6 x 18pdr	2 x 6pdr	2 x 18pdr
	22 Jul 1782	8 x 6pdr	6 x 18pdr	2 x 6pdr	2 x 24pdr
Santa Margarita	16 Mar 1780	8 x 6pdr	4 x 18pdr	2 x 6pdr	4 x 18pdr
	*c*1808		8 x 24pdr		2 x 24pdr
Monsieur	22 Jul 1782	8 x 6pdr	4 x 18pdr	2 x 6pdr	4 x 18pdr
Santa Leocadia	22 Jul 1782	8 x 6pdr	6 x 24pdr	2 x 6pdr	2 x 24pdr
Nymphe	25 Jan 1793		8 x 12pdr		4 x 12pdr
	1 Oct 1793		8 x 12pdr	1 x 6pdr	4 x 12pdr
	*c*1797		8 x 32pdr		4 x 32pdr
	*c*1808		12 x 32pdr	2 x 9pdr	2 x 32pdr
Magicienne	*c*1808		12 x 24pdr	2 x 6pdr	2 x 24pdr
28-gun ships captured 1793-1815					
Tourterelle	*c*1808		2 x 24pdr[1]		
32-gun ships captured 1793-1815					
Eurus	*c*1808		2 x 24pdr[1]		
Janus	*c*1808		8 x 24pdr	2 x 6pdr	2 x 24pdr
36-gun ships captured 1793-1815					
Oiseau	*c*1808		8 x 32pdr	2 x 6pdr	2 x 32pdr
Nereide	*c*1808		12 x 24pdr		4 x 24pdr
Santa Teresa	*c*1808		10 x 32pdr		2 x 32pdr
Franchise	*c*1808	2 x 12pdr	10 x 24pdr	2 x 12pdr	4 x 18pdr
Helder	*c*1808		10 x 32pdr	2 x 6pdr	2 x 32pdr

Notes:
[1] Upper deck armament changed to 20 x 24pdr carronades.

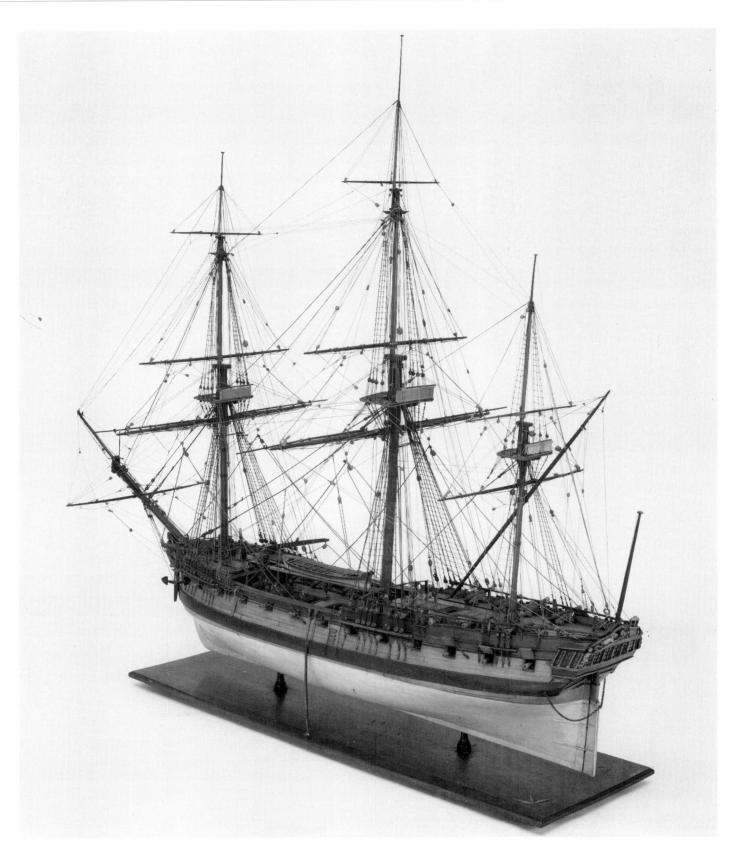

Lowestoffe of 1761, contemporary model.

One of the earliest rigged models of a frigate, this finely detailed example shows the main features of the first generation spar plan – long lateen mizzen, no mizzen topgallant or any royals, no topgallant stunsail booms, and a relatively short jibboom with a fully rigged spritsail under the bowsprit.

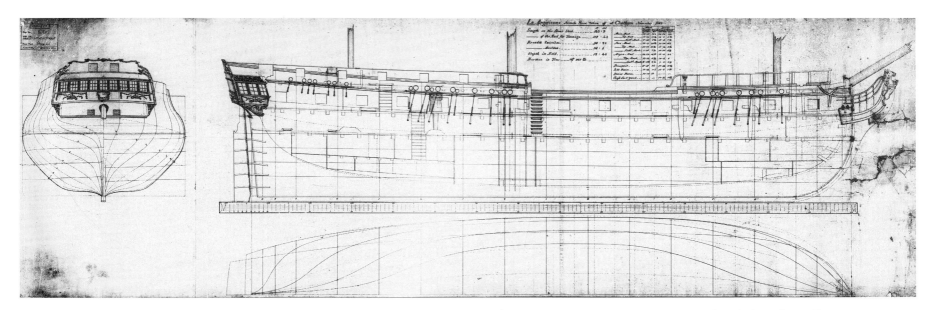

Magicienne, 36, ex-French captured 1781; as fitted sheer & profile, taken off at Chatham, November 1783.

The mast and spar dimensions of French prizes were often recorded on the draught, particularly if, like this ship, they were considerably larger than British equivalents. However, the dimensions recorded here are the cut-down sail plan carried in the Royal Navy (see Table 47).

10. *Masting and Rigging*

Frigates all carried the standard three-masted ship rig of the period, and development was confined to the extremities of the sail plan – the bowsprit, mizzen and at the heads of the masts. The first generation of ships had no mizzen topgallant mast but were issued with mizzen topgallant sails so they were presumably set 'flying' (with only a halliard and no sheets or braces) when conditions allowed. A properly fidded mast was introduced for all ships down to those of 20 guns by Admiralty Order of 24 February 1774,[62] and from about 1779 long-headed fore and main topgallant masts began to be issued, allowing a further sail to be set flying above; known initially as the 'topgallant royal' and then simply as the 'royal', this sail was also being set on the mizzen by the 1790s. Inevitably, separate fidded royal masts followed (probably around 1800) but this development is really outside the scope of this study.

The most significant change was the gradual replacement of the long lateen mizzen with a gaff and, eventually, boom fore and aft sail. By the 1750s it was common to set a cut-off version of the lateen sail with the luff laced to the mizzen mast, but the full yard was retained (its length made it a useful jury spar, and it is possible that the counterweight effect of the part before the mast reduced stress on the rigging). A gaff-headed sail had become standard on smaller, two-masted vessels, and many frigate captains began to request the shorter spar, so in 1779 the Admiralty ordered all ships of 44 guns and below to fit a gaff instead of a long mizzen.[63] Being loose-footed, this sail was restricted in size by the lead of its sheets; inside the taffrail was easiest although with a little ingenuity an iron boomkin on each quarter could extend the sail beyond the taffrail. This arrangement was not popular, and the following year the Admiralty modified its instructions for frigates to include a 'boom

sail driver in the form of a brig's mainsail', after representations from several captains that this form was 'more handy'.[64] It required an increase in the diameter of the mizzen mast by 1in to support the boom's weight, but permitted a larger sail. It was by no means universally accepted, and in 1782 the Dockyards were instructed to supply a mizzen yard or gaff as captains preferred.[65] In practice, wartime shortages meant that some ships had to take what was available if they were to get to sea promptly.

At the other end of the ship, there was little change for forty years. Initially, the 28s had not carried a spritsail topsail yard under the jibboom, but by the American War this fitting was common.[66] It is not clear if this sail was much used but the triangular headsails were, and all frigate classes were improved by the introduction of another with the flying jib and its associated boom in 1794.[67]

Although not affecting the spar plan, there were other developments to the lesser sails. In 1762 the Admiralty recognized that captains usually had their triangular staysails altered to a square-tacked form (the leg-of-mutton shape) and formulated a new Establishment.[68] From 1773 a fore and middle staysail was added to the existing suite of fore and aft sails, while topgallant stunsails were allowed over the fore and main lower and topmast stunsails (the mizzen did not set stunsails).

In Tables 46 and 47 the dimensions chosen represent the main British class at two periods in their history, while the captured ships are provided for purposes of comparison. In every case the dimensions are 'as fitted' and not merely the extrapolation from an Establishment list. However, it is worth noting that by the time of the American War British

Unidentified 36-gun frigate of *c*1800, contemporary model (left).

One of the few contemporary frigate models with sails, this cannot be identified with any specific ship but demonstrates the development of the rig by the late 1790s. There is now a flying jibboom, with a dolphin striker for the martingale stays below the bowsprit; the ship does not yet have separate royal masts, but these could be set flying from the long poleheads of the topgallants; the topsails have four rows of reef points, as ordered in 1788, while the topgallants now have stunsail booms; aft, the mizzen carries a topgallant mast and the lateen has been replaced by a gaff and boom driver.

Unidentified 36-gun frigate of *c*1800, contemporary model (above).

Besides the square sails and jibs, the model also displays the main topmast staysail (already set) with the middle staysail above, ready to be set. Because the running rigging is so detailed the model is a good source of information on the belaying points of a frigate of this era.

Table 46: MAST AND SPAR DIMENSIONS OF BRITISH FRIGATES

		Tartar, 28 1757			Aurora, 28 1785			Southampton, 32 1758			Amazon, 32 1785			Pallas & Brilliant, 36 1758 {Venus, 1777}			Triton, 32 As designed		
		Length		Diam	Length		Diam	Length		Diam	Length		Diam	Length		Diam	Length		Diam
	MASTS	yds	ins	ins	yds	ins	ins	yds	ins	ins	yds	ins	ins	yds	ins	ins	yds	ins	ins
Main	mast	27	9	22¾	27	4	23⅝	27	27	24¼	28	12	24¾	29	0	25¾	29	14	26
	topmast	16	8	15⅜	16	9	14⅜	16	16	14¾	17	0	15⅛	17	0	15¼	18	0	16⅜
	topgallant	9	5	7¾	8	4	8	8	12	8½	8	18	8½	8	18	8½	9	0	9
Fore	mast	23	30	20⅞	23	33	20⅞	24	20	21½	25	0	21⅞	25	22	23⅛	26	30	23¾
	topmast	13	20	15⅛	14	12	14⅜	14	27	14⅜	15	0	15⅛	15	12	15¼	15	30	16⅛
	topgallant	8	19	7	7	6	7	7	18	7½	7	18	7½	7	24	7⅝	7	33	7⅞
Mizzen	mast	*17	31	16	22	24	15¼	23	21	15¾	23	27	16	24	18	16⅜	?24	3	18¼
	topmast	12	27	10¾	12	7	10⅛	12	19	10⅛	12	27	10⅝	12	12	10⅛	13	18	11¼
	topgallant	5	31	5¾	†5	20	6				†5	29	6⅜	{6	8	6¼}	6	27	6¾
	pole head				2	12					2	16							
Bowsprit		17	0	23¼	16	29	23⅞	16	32	25¼	17	20	25	17	0	25½	16	22	27¼
Jibboom		12	3	9½	11	27	10¼	12	18	11	12	10	10¾	12	18	11	12	22	10⅞
	YARDS																		
Main	yard	24	25	16½	23	27	16⅜	25	0	17	24	28	17⅛	25	21	18	26	0	18
	topsail yard	18	0	11⅞	17	21	11	18	25	11½	18	12	11⅜	18	28	11⅝	19	8	12
	topgallant yard	12	18	6¼	10	25	6⅜	11	11	6⅝	11	6	6⅝	12	0	6⅝	11	26	7¼
Fore	yard	21	21	14⅜	20	26	14¼	21	30	15	21	22	15	22	6	15½	22	25	15¾
	topsail yard	16	26	11	15	16	9¾	16	10	10⅛	16	6	10	16	28	10½	16	33	10⅝
	topgallant yard	11	0	5⅜	9	16	5⅝	10	0	6	9	30	5⅞	10	16	6⅛	10	12	6¼
Mizzen	(lateen)	22	0	10¾	21	14	11½	22	18	11¾	22	11	11½	23	7	12½			
	topsail yard	12	7	6⅝	11	26	6⅝	12	12	6⅛	12	9	6⅞	12	20	7¾	12	30	7¾
	topgallant yard	8	6	5¼	8	3	5				8	16	5¼	{8	24	5¼}			
	crossjack	17	26	8¾	15	16	9¾	16	10	10⅛	16	6	10	16	28	10½	16	33	10⅜
Spritsail yard		17	29	10½	15	16	9¾	16	10	10⅛	16	6	10	16	28	10½	16	33	10⅜
Sprit topsail yard		[9	32	5⅞]	9	16	5⅝	10	0	6	9	30	5⅞	{10	16	6⅛}	10	12	6¼
[Mizzen gaff					9	18	5⅝				9	30	5⅞	[12	20	11½]	11	32	10⅛
Driver boom]					10	30	9¾				11	24	10						
[Flying jibboom]					[9	28	5⅞]				[10	8	6⅛]	[10	26	6½]			

*from the upper deck   † to the stop

Source		NMM ADM/B/156	NMM SPB/37b	NMM POR/A/19	NMM SPB/37b	NMM POR/D/19 {NMM POR/D/21}	Draught ZAZ3076

Notes:

By Admiralty Order of 1 June 1779 all ships of 44 guns and below to have a gaff in lieu of a lateen mizzen.

By Admiralty Order of 29 June 1780 all frigates were to have the diameter of the mizzen increased by 1in to compensate for the extra weight of the driver boom.

Flying jibbooms were issued by Admiralty Order of 18 Aug 1794.

Dimensions are given above [in brackets] for changes to surviving ships of each class.

Table 47: MAST AND SPAR DIMENSIONS OF CAPTURED FRIGATES

		Bellona, 30 As capt 1747			Delaware, 28 As fitted 1781			Repulse, 32 As fitted 1759			Magicienne, 32 As capt 1781			Magicienne, 32 In Royal Navy			Confederate, 36 3 Oct 1781 [1]		
		Length		Diam	Length		Diam	Length		Diam	Length		Diam	Length		Diam	Length		Diam
	MASTS	yds	ins	ins	yds	ins	ins	yds	ins	ins	yds	ins	ins	yds	ins	ins	yds	ins	ins
Main	mast	27	11	23½	25	6	24¼	28	6	25¼	29	27	26½	29	12	26¼	30	24	29
	topmast	17	21	15	16	3	15¼	17	0	15½	19	17¼	16	17	24	15¾	17	27	16
	topgallant	10	25	8½	9	4	8	8	12	8¾	12	27	8½	8	30	8¾	8	30	8⅞
Fore	mast	24	35	21¾	23	8	22¼	24	32	22¼	27	9¾	24½	26	0	23⅜	27	6	26⅞
	topmast	15	27	13½	14	33	15⅛	15	2	15½	18	2¼	14¾	15	22	15¾	16	2	16
	topgallant	9	9	6⅝	8	14	7½	7	18	7½	11	18¼	7½	7	28	7¾	8	1	8⅛
Mizzen	mast	24	28	15½	21	30	18¾	23	12	16½	21	15½	18½	24	28	16⅞	26	3	19⅜
	topmast	12	30	9¾	16	31	10¼	12	19	10⅛	13	16½	11¾	13	14	11¾	13	19	11⅛
	topgallant	8	0	4⅝										6	26	6⅞			
	pole head																		
Bowsprit		15	12	24¼	15	25	23¾	16	31	25¼	17	0	25½	17	18	26	18	25	28½
Jibboom		11	27	9¾	12	15	10¾	12	0	10½	13	3¾	11¾	12	34	11½	13	8	11⅞
	YARDS																		
Main	yard	24	0	18	22	10	15¾	25	0	17	27	35¼	21	26	26	18¼	27	26	19¼
	topsail yard	18	0	12	16	26	10¼	18	25	11⅛	19	30	13¼	19	6	11⅞	20	9	12½
	topgallant yard	11	12	7	10	32	7¼	12	0	6⅝	13	29¼	7	12	6	7⅜	12	8	7⅜
Fore	yard	21	24	15¾	20	27	14¾	21	30	15	25	5¼	19	23	10	16¼	24	5	16⅞
	topsail yard	14	26	10½	15	9	10¼	16	10	10⅛	17	25½	12	17	14	10¾	17	20	11⅝
	topgallant yard	9	10	6¼	10	14	6¼	10	0	6	12	27	6½	10	26	6¾	10	18	6¼
Mizzen	(lateen)	21	9	11				22	18	11¾	24	28½	15				24	30	13¾
	topsail yard	13	6	8¼	12	0	7½	12	12	6⅞	14	31½	7½	13	6	8	13	13	8¼
	topgallant yard	5	19	4⅜			9	0	5⅜					9	0	5⅜			
	crossjack	17	18	9¼	16	18	10½	16	10	10⅛	18	27¾	12	17	14	10¾	17	20	11⅝
Spritsail yard		16	0	11½	9	18	6	16	10	10⅛	17	32	12	17	14	10¾	17	20	11⅝
Sprit topsail yard											14	6	7	12	6	7⅜	0	18	6¼
[Mizzen gaff					12	0	10⅛							12	0	9½			
driver boom]														20	12	12			
[Flying jibboom]																			
Source		NMM ADM/B/135			PRO Adm 95/77			NMM POR/A/20			NMM RUSI/NM/42			NMM POR/D/21			PRO Adm 106/2790		

Notes:

[1] These dimensions are substantially smaller than those quoted by Chapelle (*American Sailing Navy*, p85), apparently from Admiralty sources, but on 11 April 1782 the ship was ordered to have 'the same drop of canvas as a 50-gun ship.' (PRO Adm 106/2792).

This table is a small selection of available dimensions. Others surviving (with their sources) include:

Lys, 1745 and *Deux Couronnes*, 1747 (NMM ADM/B/131 & 135), *Rostan*, 1758 and *Melampe*, 1758 (NMM POR/A/19), *Blonde*, 1760 (NMM POR/A/20), *Fortunée*, 1779 (NMM RUSI/NM/42) and *Monsieur*, 1780 (NMM POR/D/22).

Brune in 1779 (PRO Adm 95/96) and *Alcmene* in 1781 (PRO Adm 106/2791) were masted as English 28s like *Aurora* in Table 46, even though it represented a significant reduction over the original French dimensions.

Spar dimensions are also listed on some draughts, including: *Braak*, 1800; *Heldin*, 1810; *Mars*, 1781; 1783; *Prudente*, 1777; *Santa Leocadia*, 1781; *Topaze*, 1795; and *Helder*, 1810. These are usually dimensions as captured but *Prudente*, unusually, also quotes the as fitted figures for comparison.

classes of each rate followed a standard spar plan, whatever the design (the larger *Hermione* class were masted exactly as the *Active*s, or surviving *Niger*s, for example). Furthermore, while there was a tendency to retain 'as captured' dimensions for prizes during the Seven Years War, the pressures of the later conflict largely prohibited this form of bespoke tailoring: short-term but often acute supply difficulties made for numerous exceptions, but the generalisation holds good.

It is almost inevitable with the introduction of an entirely new type of ship that some experimentation would be necessary before the mast sizes would be satisfactory. The usual British system of casting dimensions was ultimately a function of the ship's breadth, but frigates carried a lower weight of metal (although at a greater freeboard) than existing types and could afford to carry proportionately more canvas. The 28s seem to have had their dimensions calculated from those of their model, the *Tygre*, and occasioned no complaints,[69] but the first 32s and 36s had no real precedents and used the conservative proportions of the existing Establishments. In May 1757 Captain Gilchrist of the *Southampton* requested that his yards be increased to the proportions of the 28s, but a more powerful voice was soon heard when Anson complained that the 36s and 32s in his squadron were under-canvassed, suggesting an increase of 4ft and 3ft respectively to their main masts and all other spars in proportion. This was duly ordered in September 1757, and it is these revised dimensions that are given in Table 44. Anson specifically excepted the Bately-designed *Richmond* and *Thames*, which may, therefore, have been masted differently[70], but the latter was undergoing her own alterations in September, when 18in were added to the hoist of the topgallants, and the crossjack extended by 5ft to prevent it getting inside the backstays.

Numerous detail alterations to the new frigates continued to be made for most of the war; these largely concerned the setting up of the standing rigging – the length and position of channels, number of deadeyes, and steeve of the bowsprit, for example. However, the period of trial-and-error came to a close with the new rigging Establishment of 1773, and the rather conservative designs of the American War period built on the experience of twenty years with similar ships.

11. Performance

It is widely believed that the performance under sail of British warships in the eighteenth century was inferior to that of its opponents. This is largely based on anecdotal evidence and no real attempt has ever been made to quantify this assumption, despite the fact that copious evidence exists in the form of detailed Sailing Quality Reports that survive for most ships, including prizes, from about 1740 onwards.[71]

An example of a report form is reproduced as Table 48 so it suffices to point out that the main concern is with speeds on each point of sailing; manoeuvrability; seaworthiness; and optimum trim. Towards the end of the century, when ships carried more ballast, the reports became slightly longer, with more questions devoted to stowage and the setting up of the masts and rigging, but the principal questions remained the same for the whole of the period under review.

The reports were compiled by the ship's captain usually at the end of a commission and served two separate functions: sailing ships were subtle machines that required considerable 'fine tuning' and these

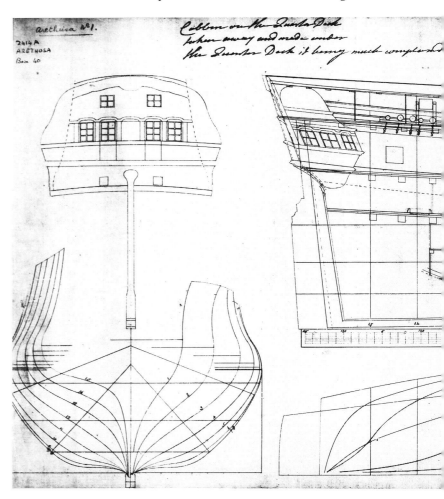

reports enabled ship-handling experience to be passed on from commanding officers to their successors; however, copies of the reports were ultimately lodged with the Navy Board so they were obviously intended to give the ship's designers a 'user's' view of its strong points and weaknesses. If British ships really were inferior, it was not for want of information.

Because these reports were not truly objective, in the sense of readings off monitoring instruments, they have to be used with care, but it is not difficult to recognize – and discount – exaggeration or prejudice. They sought the best recorded performance of each ship over a relatively long period, so this tends to even out anomalies and extremes, and makes comparisons between ships more meaningful.

Based on a thorough analysis of relevant reports, the characteristics of British 12pdr and 9pdr frigate classes are given in résumé form in the accompanying Table 49, along with a selection of captured ships chosen because either they are written up in particular detail or they manifest significant attributes; some notes on the preceding 24-gun Sixth Rates are included to demonstrate the degree of improvement represented by the new frigates. Readers may draw their own conclusions from a perusal of these data, but there are a few generalities that warrant expanded comment.

CONSISTENCY OF PERFORMANCE WITHIN CLASSES

The arrangement of ballast and stowage, the set-up of masts and rigging, the progressive effects of fouling, and the ship-handling skills of her officers all influenced the sailing qualities of a wooden warship. Even taking all this into account, it is clear from the Sailing Quality Reports that ships built to the same draught (*ie* of the same class) had similar characteristics. It is perhaps clearest for the large classes where there is a greater sample of evidence, and a norm is more easily established.

This is not to say that they were all identical by any means – in any modern fleet of single-class yachts there are often one or two consistent

Arethusa, 32, ex-French *Arethuse*, as captured sheer & profile draught 1759.

In many respects a typical French frigate of the Seven Years War period, *Arethusa* was a good fair weather performer, but was vulnerable if pressed. The ship lost a number of masts to stress of weather during her British service and one captain believed this was encouraged by the lack of support from the characteristically French shallow hull and an extreme tumblehome that did not allow sufficient spread to the shrouds. Note the small quarterdeck cabin: a note on the draught says it was removed, 'it being much complained of'.

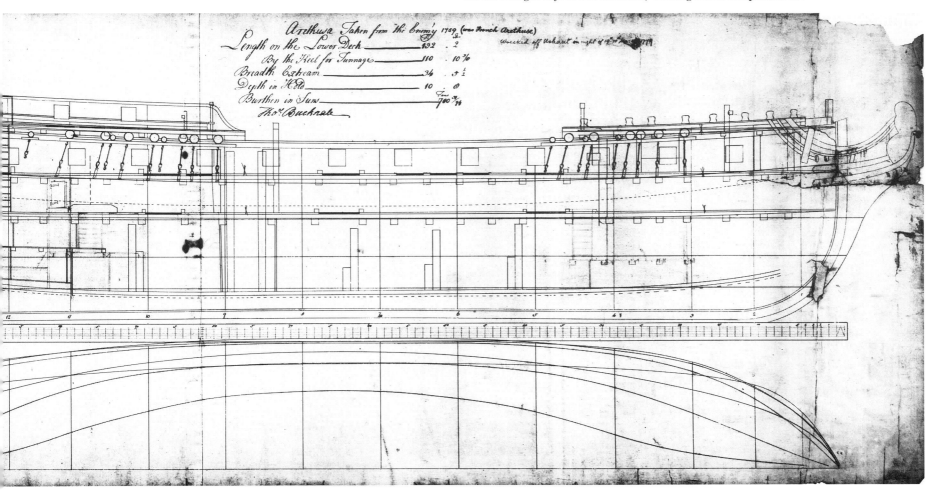

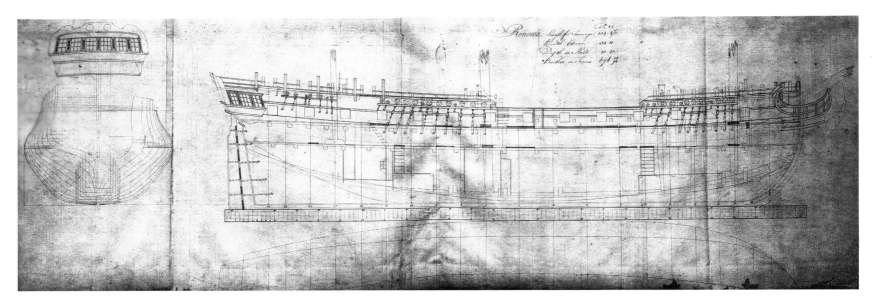

***Renown*, 30, ex-French *Renommée*, captured 1747; sheer & profile draught as repaired (?1757-8).**

One of the first French frigate-built ships and one of the best under sail, *Renown* was notably faster than anything in the Royal Navy of the time. She was a popular cruiser for twenty-five years, although her sailing qualities in her later years showed a marked decline. This deterioration may have been aided by a major repair the ship received in 1757-8 (for details, compare this draught with the 'as captured' sheer in Chapter 1); apart from an alteration to the rake of the sternpost and a modified cutwater profile, the underwater body was untouched, but the reconstructed topsides and extra upper deck port may well have added weight. Unfortunately, this draught does not show a load waterline, but other evidence suggests that there was no significant change to the laden draught of water. *(The Science Museum, London)*

race winners, which may not necessarily be in the hands of the yacht club's best skippers; nevertheless, the variations in performance between individual members of the class are markedly less than those between different classes. So it was with the eighteenth-century frigate: a big class often had its 'stars' and its occasional 'slug' but, assuming the ships were properly set up, the difference was not great. Recorded speeds show some variation, which often depended on the weather met (furthermore, it was almost inevitable given the crudity of measurement,[72]) but general characteristics like manoeuvrability, weatherliness and seaworthiness remain consistent across all members of the class.

It should not be surprising to find that ships designed as a class perform as a class, but in recent years a scepticism has grown up about the effect of hull form on speed and handling.[73] The designers were so restricted by the displacement requirement, runs the argument, that variations to the hull lines could have made very little difference. The evidence of the Sailing Quality Reports suggests the opposite: there are differences between classes – often, it has to be admitted, not very great, but significant – and in a world where 24-hour chases were not uncommon a consistent ½kt advantage could make all the difference.

A STEP BACKWARDS: THE SECOND GENERATION OF BRITISH FRIGATES

If hull design does have a bearing on performance, then success in naval architecture becomes a matter of skill, not luck, and some of its practitioners must be regarded as more talented than others. It is notable that the first frigates were a distinct advance over the old 24-gun Sixth Rates, but the new ships were both larger and of a different internal layout which substantially reduced their topside area. In this context it is perhaps far more significant that the designs of Williams or Hunt were actually inferior to those of their predecessor Slade. The basic

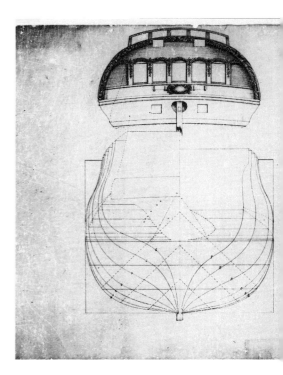

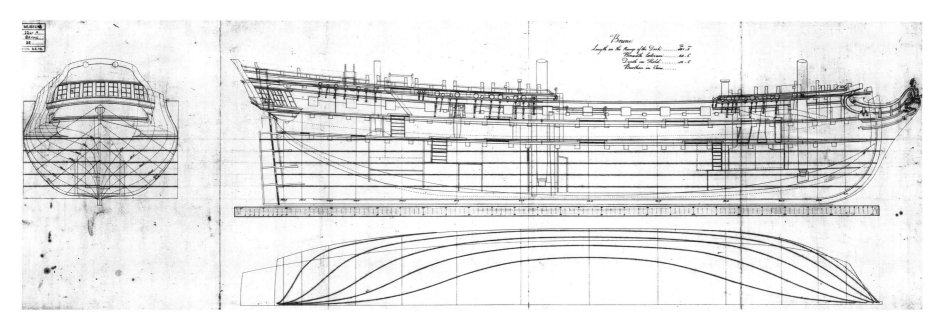

Brune, 32, ex-French, captured 1761; sheer & profile draught as repaired 1770-72) (above).

This ship enjoyed a long career in the Royal Navy but required a high expenditure in maintenance including the Great Repair represented by this draught (the 'as captured' draught can be found in Chapter 8). Like so many French frigates of this generation, the ship was a good fair weather performer but a decidedly poor sea-boat in heavier conditions – and since typical British service included long and arduous sea-time, the lightly constructed hull was always vulnerable to racking stresses, which explains the large sums expended on her upkeep. The Great Repair almost certainly involved structural strengthening and the ship gained about 6 inches mean draught at full load.

Albemarle, 28, ex-French *Menagère*, captured 1778; sheer & profile draught as taken off at Portsmouth Dockyard, July 1781 (below).

This ship has neither the hull form nor the proportions of a genuine frigate and was in fact the French navy's largest *flûte*, or storeship, although even in this role she was armed with 28 guns. In this light, her performance is not as poor as it might at first sight appear. Indeed, the need to press into cruising service such unsuitable ships indicates the desperate measures forced on the Royal Navy when so heavily outnumbered by the French-Spanish-Dutch naval alliance supporting the struggle for American independence.

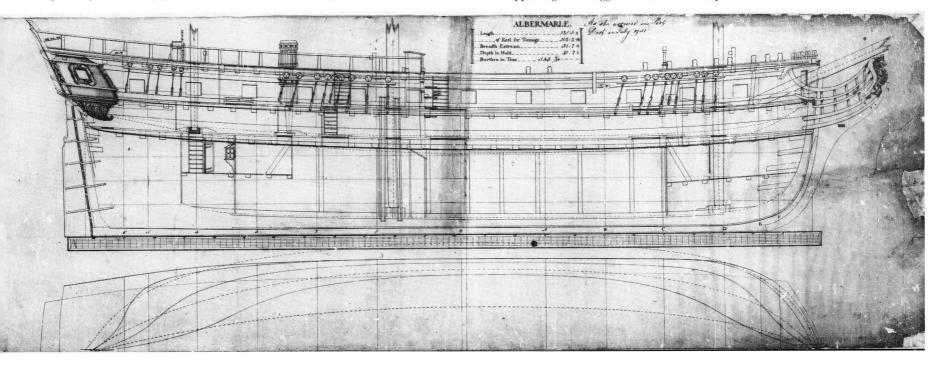

specifications for the 28s and the 32s in essence remained unchanged, and although the later ships were called upon to carry greater topside weights (extra boats, carronades, more solid upperworks, and heavier ballast to compensate,[74]) the advent of copper sheathing should have offset the deficiency. In fact it appears that coppering added little pure speed compared to an unsheathed ship fresh out of dock but greatly retarded the onset of fouling and so preserved ship speed for far longer. In the case of the frigates of the American War period, coppering may have disguised their mediocrity for a generation, but it is equally likely that the problem was recognized (Hunt replaced his *Active* class quite quickly) but that the overstretched resources of the Surveyors' office could not cope with too many changes.[75] Certainly from the 1790s strenuous efforts were made to improve the sailing qualities of British frigates, notably by making them proportionately longer.

RELATIVE QUALITIES OF BRITISH AND FRENCH FRIGATES

While it is highly likely that the first French frigates were superior in most respects to the Establishment 24-gun ships, a comparison of the sailing qualities of British and French frigates during the Seven Years War clearly demonstrates that the advantage had been wiped out. Even in the American War there was no clear French superiority, nor were the few American frigates captured regarded as anything special.[76]

Raleigh, 32, ex-American, captured 1778; sheer & profile draught taken off at Plymouth Dockyard, October 1779.

Very few merchantmen were as large as a frigate so there can have been very little direct experience of major ship design in the American colonies in 1776. In the circumstances, therefore, the first Continental frigate programme produced some very creditable ships, although none of the objective evidence suggests that they were in any way outstanding performers under sail. *Raleigh*, for example, was a moderate fair-weather ship, but poor in heavier conditions.

Grana, 28, ex-Spanish, as captured sheer & profile draught taken off at Plymouth Dockyard, May 1781.

In general Spanish cruisers needed British-style seakeeping and endurance – Spanish territories were still the most far-flung of all European empires – rather than smooth-water speed. As a result, although the proportions and hull forms resembled their French equivalents, they were less extreme. In order to retain the advantages of a relatively long hull with structural strength, Spanish ships tended to be very large for their gun-power: *Grana*, for example, carried a main armament of only twenty-two 6pdrs when captured.

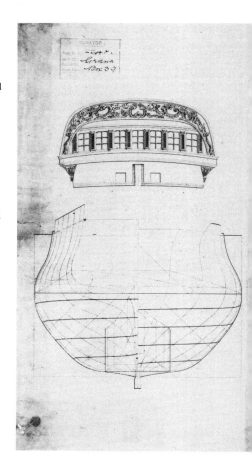

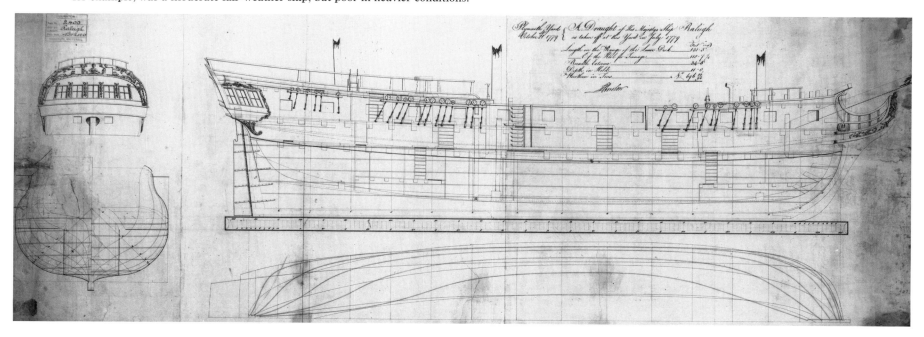

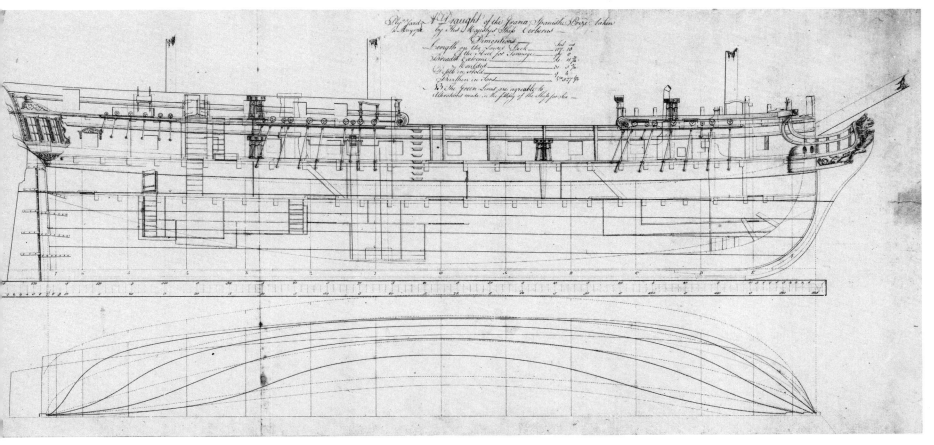

In the final analysis, it is almost impossible for one ship to outsail another of broadly similar design on every point of sailing and in every condition of wind and sea. This means that 'superiority' can only apply to specific aspects of performance, and it is far more significant to look at the areas in which British and French ships seem to excel. Like the ships themselves, the matter is subtle since so many variables are involved, but there do appear to be distinctly different emphases in the sailing qualities of the two nations' cruising ships.[77]

The reports on British classes all stress their performance in a seaway and/or strong winds, whereas the French vessels exhibit a strong preference for smooth water, and to a lesser extent, lighter winds. In general the sailing qualities of many British classes improved as conditions became more boisterous; even the sluggardly *Southampton*s became relatively faster as wind and sea rose, and the *Richmond*s became more weatherly. In contrast, many French ships were said to dislike heavy weather, and frigates like *Bellone* and *Brune* suffered dramatic loss of speed in such conditions. Furthermore, most French vessels rolled and/or pitched greatly and shipped water, whereas the motions of British vessels was much easier and consequently they tended to be much drier.

Even the poorest sailers among the British classes were manoeuvrable, being quick and usually dependable to stay [tack] and wear, which would be important in the kind of tacking duel that opened many single-ship engagements. Although not universally true, many French frigates were slow in stays (and very few would wear quickly), which was almost certainly a result of their longer, shallower hulls.

While French frigates were noted for their speed, they were not particularly weatherly (*Blonde* and *Danae*, for example) and some were explicitly stated to be leewardly (*Bellone* and *Vestale*); in the Royal Navy this was put down to their relatively shallow draught. However, the very format of the Sailing Quality Reports stresses the importance of wind-ward performance for British vessels, and even the slower classes like the *Southampton*s were weatherly; this advantage tended to increase in rough water. This may explain why the relatively leewardly French vessels were not outstanding performers close-hauled; even the all-round excellence of *L'Abenakise* did not extend to this point of sailing.

The characteristics of the *Tweed* are particularly noteworthy for in many ways she was a British attempt to build a typical French frigate – long, low and light. It is significant that she was faster than even the *Niger*s on her chosen point of sailing, but that her superiority did not apply when close-hauled, or in heavy weather. She proved to be a wet, lively and uncomfortable cruiser, was tender, and her rolling and pitching soon strained the lightly-built hull. She was not ideal for the rigours of, say, blockade duty and her utility was further reduced by the fact that she could not stow anywhere near the Foreign Service allowance of stores. Apart from being rather more weatherly, in terms of her sailing qualities, she was a fairly representative of French frigates – faster than British vessels in optimum conditions, but a poorer and less robust sea-boat.

Summing up, it can be said that French cruisers emphasised speed, especially in light conditions, but often at the expense of a sea-kindly hull; British frigates, though not always as fast in smooth water, tended to be more weatherly, and were better all-round performers and especially in heavy weather.

Table 48: SAILING QUALITY REPORT FORM

Observations of Qualities of His Majesty's ship — *[usually also gives commander and date]*

Her best sailing Draft of Water, when Victualled and Stored for Channel service — afore, — aft, or as much lighter (at the same Difference) as She is able to bear Sail. Her lowest Gundeck ports will then be above the Surface of the water —, After port —, Fore ditto —.

Query the first. How she behaves close haul'd and how many knots she runs:

| In a topgallant gale |
| In a topsail gale |
| How she steers, and how she wears and stays |
| Under her | Reefed topsails |
| | Reefed courses |

And query, whether she will stay under her courses

Query the 2nd. In each circumstance above mentioned (in sailing with other ships) in what Proportion she gathers to windward, and in what proportion she forereaches, and in general her proportion of leeway

Query the 3rd. How she proves in Sailing thro' all Variations of the Wind from its being a point or Two Abaft the Beam, to its veering forward upon the Bowline in every Strength of Gale, especially in a Stiff Gale and a head Sea; and how many Knots she runs in each Circumstance; and how she carries her Helm

Query the 4th. The most Knots she runs before the Wind; and how she rolls in the Trough of the Sea

Query the 5th. How she behaves in lying-to or under a try, under a Main Sail and also under a Mizon ballanc'd

Query the 6th. What for a Roader she is, and how she careens

Query the 7th. If upon Trial the best sailing Draft of Water given as above should not prove to be so, what is her best sailing Draft of Water — afore, — abaft

Query the 8th. What is her Draft of Water when victualled to six Months, and stored for Foreign Service — afore, — abaft

Query the 9th. What Height is her lowest Gundeck Port then above the Surface of the Water

Query the 10th. The Trim of the ship

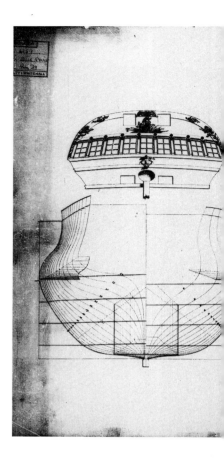

Belle Poule, 36, ex-French, as captured sheer & profile draught taken off at Portsmouth, November 1780.

During the Seven Years War there was little feeling in the Royal Navy that French frigates were superior under sail to their British opponents, but the doubts began to surface once again during the American War. One of the best French examples was *Belle Poule*, although she was regarded as exceptional even in the French navy. Note *Belle Poule*'s complete absence of protection for quarterdeck and forecastle, the guns being secured between chocks; this doubtless enhanced performance but would have been a grave disadvantage in action.

[These were the original questions, but from the 1790s an expanded form was often employed with the following additional queries about stowage and stability]

Query the 11th. How she stands under her sails

Query the 12th. The Quantities of Iron and Shingle Ballast on board

Query the 13th. How she stores her provisions and water, and what quantities of the latter she carries with four and six months provisions; also the quantities of shingle or iron ballast which may be put out when she is victualled for six months

Query the 14th. The weight of the Provisions taken on Board in Consequence of being stored for the above time

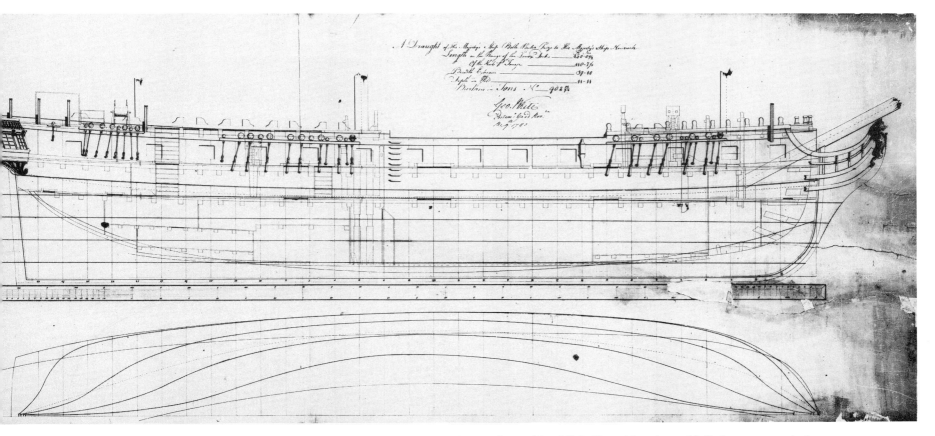

Table 49: SAILING QUALITIES OF ENGLISH FRIGATES

The following summaries of sailing qualities are preceded by examples of trim, quoting the resulting freeboard of the midships gunport (a major preoccupation of contemporary reports). Wherever possible, the lightest and deepest loadings are given by way of contrast and the time and service for which stored (CS = Channel Service and FS = Foreign Service); these may reveal some inconsistencies and it is clear that the measuring was not always carried out with great care. In the descriptions of sailing qualities, the points of sailing (reaching, running etc) are those familiar to the modern sailor, rather than the terminology of the time.

Sixth Rates, 24 guns, Establishment period

	Draught fwd	Draught aft	Midships port above water	Stored for service
Surprize	15ft 2in	14ft 3in	2ft 6in	3 months [CS]
Triton	14ft 3in	13ft 9in	3ft 3in	3 months [CS]

The 1741 Establishment: these ships were not built to a single draught so generalisations are difficult, but if anything they were a touch faster than their successors (*Centaur* registered 12kts before the wind). Windward performance was indifferent, while manoeuvrability ranged from the adequate to the poor.

The 1745 Establishment: it is easy to see why this was a disappointment – none was very fast, 9kts close-hauled in a topgallant gale being near the top of the range, although *Sphinx* claimed 10kts in a topsail gale (against this *Queenborough* never exceeded 5kts). They seem to have been a little crank so could not be pressed, but were generally weatherly, although their best point of sailing was beam- or broad-reaching (*Sphynx* had once managed 13kts, but this was exceptional). Not very handy and only moderate sea-boats.

Improved 24s: neither Allin's *Mermaid* nor Acworth's *Seahorse* was a marked improvement over the 1745 ships, although *Mermaid* was possibly the better ship (10kts close-hauled and 11½kts on a beam reach compared with 8kts and 11-12kts running). Both were leewardly, the *Seahorse* in particular, and neither was a good heavy weather performer; they were reasonably handy, but in virtually every respect they were eclipsed by the *Unicorn*, which in effect was the competing design.

The 1741 ships based on reports on *Surprize* (undated c1748 and Sep 1754); *Deal Castle* (9 May 1750); *Centaur* (Sep 1749); *Rye* (17 Aug 1751); *Syren* (28 May 1752); *Triton* (5 Jun 1755). The 1745 ships based on Reports on *Arundel* (2 Oct 1751 and 29 Nov 1757); *Hind* (28 Sep 1756); *Sphinx* (31 Oct 1754); *Queenborough* (28 Sep 1752).

The Improved 24s based on reports on *Mermaid* (26 Jul 1753); *Seahorse* (8 Mar 1760).

Unicorn class, 28 guns, 1747

	Draught fwd	Draught aft	Midships port above water	Stored for service
Unicorn	13ft 8in	16ft 4in	5ft 4in	3 months [CS]
Tartar	15ft 3in	16ft 7in	5ft 6in	6 months [FS]
Carysfort	14ft 0in	16ft 10in	6ft 0in	4 months [FS]

Very fast and weatherly: 9-10kts close-hauled in a topgallant gale making only half a point leeway, to 12-13kts broad-reaching or running. The later ships were not quite as fast as the *Unicorn* herself, but *Tartar* was close and *Hussar* was superior to anything else in company except *L'Abenakise*, which was faster directly before the wind; the fir-built ships showed no marked differences in performance, but needed extra ballast for optimum trim. Very manoeuvrable, steering easily and *Unicorn* 'stays [tacks] in her own length' and was very dependable going about. Stiff, but easy in a seaway, rolling easily if deeply and shipping very little water. Good foul-weather ships, *Lizard* having clawed her way off a lee shore at 4kts under reefed courses in a very hard gale [Force 9]; noticeably more weatherly than other ships in these conditions. Behaved best when trimmed deep.

Based on reports on *Unicorn* (17 Jun 1751 and 30 Sep 1756); *Tartar* (23 Jan 1758 and 12 Apr 1763); *Lizard* (17 Dec 1773, 12 Sep 1782 and undated c1794); *Maidstone* (8 Aug 1766 and 14 Dec 1781); *Hussar* (undated c1760); *Boreas* (1 Sep 1757); *Shannon* (21 Jan 1763); *Actaeon* (20 Dec 1762); *Trent* (9 Sep 1763); *Cerberus* 13 Jul 1763); *Milford* (2 Mar 1781); *Guadeloupe* 2 Sep 1772); *Carysfort* (26 Jul 1783).

Southampton class, 32 guns, 1756

	Draught fwd	Draught aft	Midships port above water	Stored for service
Diana	15ft 10in	16ft 10in	6ft 11in	6 months [FS]
Southampton	15ft 3in	16ft 3in	7ft 5½ in	4 months [CS]

Not as fast or as weatherly as contemporary frigate classes in light conditions: 7-8kts close-hauled in a topgallant gale to 12kts before the wind. Better in a blow: of *Southampton* it was said, 'in reefed topsail weather few or no ships can carry more sail or keep a better wind', and would tend to fore-reach under courses alone on ships that were otherwise superior. However, very manoeuvrable – quick in staying and wearing, going about in a short distance. Good sea-boats, pitching easily in a seaway, and being very stiff would sail faster in these conditions as more canvas was pressed upon them. They may have been faster originally: an early report on *Vestal* claims 9-9½kts close-hauled in a topgallant gale and 14kts before the wind, but that was 'when the bottom was single, but since it has been sheathed, and her sides laden with topriders and much iron, we have found that she goes less in every point of sailing by a knot and a half at least.'

Based on reports on *Southampton* (14 Feb 1763, 6 Jun 1778 and 6 Nov 1782); *Vestal* (Apr 1763); *Diana* (25 Jun 1763, Dec 1773 and 9 Jun 1792).

Richmond class, 32 guns, 1756

	Draught fwd	Draught aft	Midships port above water	Stored for service
Jason	17ft 2in	17ft 1in	7ft 0in	6 months [FS]
Boston	15ft 2in	16ft 1in	7ft 9in	3 months [CS]

Slightly faster than *Southamptons*: 10-11kts close-hauled in topgallant gale, 12kts on a beam reach (generally regarded as their best point of sailing but 13kts running, with studding sails set, was recorded). Fast and dependable in staying and wearing. Weatherly, but this advantage over other frigate classes became more marked as the wind increased – of *Thames* it was said, 'the harder it blows she is more weatherly'. Remarkably dry ships in high seas.

Based on reports on *Juno* (20 Feb 1772); *Thames* (21 Sep 1781 and 11 Apr 1792); *Boston* (26 Mar 1763, 29 Jul 1772 and 17 Jul 1782); *Larke* (26 Mar 1763); *Jason* (27 Apr 1767 and 8 Oct 1771).

Niger class, 32 guns, 1757

	Draught fwd	Draught aft	Midships port above water	Stored for service
Stag	16ft 11in	17ft 2in	5ft 11in	8 months [FS]
Stag	14ft 8in	16ft 11in	7ft 7¾in	4 months [CS]

The star performers of the first generation of English frigates, exhibiting all-round excellence. Very fast: 10-11kts close-hauled in topgallant gale, 13½kts with wind just abaft the beam, 12kts running (their worst point of sailing). Remarkably weatherly, making only ¼ point leeway with all sails drawing. Sailed best when deeply laden. Highly manoeuvrable, staying quickly without any loss of way and able to wear in four

times the ships' length. Tendency to pitch in a steep head sea, but otherwise liked heavy weather, when they were stiff, rolled easily and shipped little water – in strong winds could carry sail 'as long as the masts would bear it', without detriment to their speed, and gained even greater advantage over other classes as conditions worstened. Not surprisingly, the best performance was recorded by *Alarm* after coppering, but the margin was only about ½kt over the best of her uncoppered sisters (*Niger* was said to outsail any frigate except those coppered).

Based on reports on *Niger* (undated c1780 and 16 Jan 1799); *Alarm* (Jul 1763 and undated c1770); *Aeolus* (16 Nov 1763 and Jan 1784); *Stag* (24 Apr 1772); *Montreal* (18 Nov 1767); *Quebec* (8 May 1763 and Aug 1772); *Emerald* (18 Mar 1763); *Pearl* (undated c1780 and 31 Aug 1792); *Winchelsea* (undated c1786 and 6 Nov 1794); *Apollo* ex-*Glory* (21 Dec 1780).

Tweed, 32 guns, 1757

	Draught fwd	Draught aft	Midships port above water	Stored for service
Tweed	13ft 8in	16ft 7in	6ft 4in	3 months [CS]

Very fast: 10kts close-hauled in a topgallant gale and once recorded 13kts when 6 months foul. Weatherly but very wet on a bowline, but in smooth water with a quartering wind reckoned to fore reach and weather on a squadron consisting of *Stag* and a trio of *Unicorns* (12 miles every 24 hours). Running was her worst point of sailing, although she was still fast. Reasonably manoeuvrable, and dependable in wearing. Not a good heavy weather ship, plunged deeply in a head sea, was tender and although she rolled easily she 'strained her upperworks, being slight built'. Would not stow anything like 6 months provisions.

Based on reports of 19 Jan 1760 and 23 Aug 1763.

Pallas class, 36 guns, 1756

	Draught fwd	Draught aft	Midships port above water	Stored for service
Pallas	16ft 0in	16ft 9in	7ft 1½in	4 months [FS]
Pallas	15ft 9in	16ft 8in	7ft 4½in	3 months [CS]

Faster (12½-13kts in a stiff gale on a broad reach, and 10kts close-hauled), but otherwise comparable with *Southamptons*. Not outstandingly weatherly, but generally very manoeuvrable. Good heavy weather ships and would carry sail in most conditions. In 1770 the captain of *Venus* considered, 'The ship is overmasted and when it blows fresh is impeded in her going by much sail. Known her go 1½kts the faster for having the mainsail up and the topgallant sails in going large.'

Based on reports on *Pallas* (18 Apr 1758 and undated c1760); *Venus* (1 Nov 1760, 18 Jun 1770, 13 Apr 1772 and 1 Jun 1786); *Brilliant* (19 Mar 1763).

Mermaid class, 28 guns, 1760

	Draught fwd	Draught aft	Midships port above water	Stored for service
Boreas	15ft 11in	16ft 4in	6ft 4in	4 months [CS]

Generally, not very fast (12kts is the highest quoted, before the wind); mediocre sailing free, but very good performance to windward, managing 10-11kts close-hauled in a topgallant gale. Speed held up relatively well in heavy weather, and they rolled deep but easy. Good, but not exceptional, manoeuvrability.

Based on reports on *Mermaid* (Apr 1763); *Hussar* (1771); *Solebay* (2 Mar 1780 and undated c1780); *Triton* (1 Nov 1795); *Boreas* (29 Nov 1784).

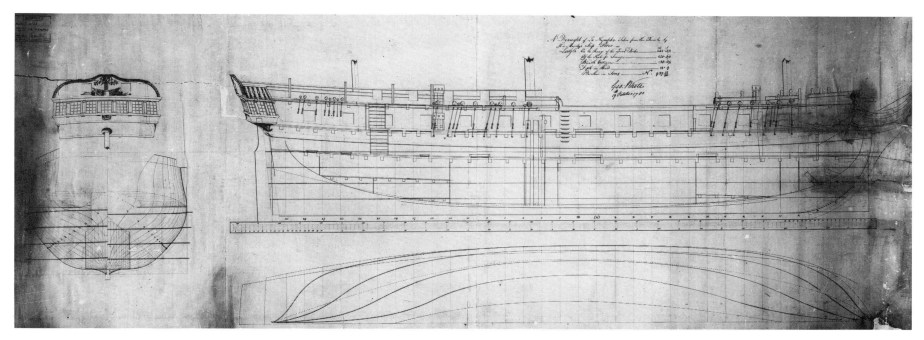

Nymphe, 36, ex-French, as captured sheer & profile draught taken off at Portsmouth, October 1780.

Perhaps typical of the French frigates of her generation, *Nymphe* was fast in light conditions but did not enjoy bad weather. If anything, French frigates of the 1770s seem to be no more of an advance over their predecessors than the equivalent British classes.

Lowestoffe class, 32 guns, 1760

	Draught fwd	Draught aft	Midships port above water	Stored for service
Lowestoffe	16ft 5in	16ft 7in	7ft 4in	4 months [CS]
Diamond	16ft 6in	16ft 10in	8ft 2½in	3 months [CS]

In most respects a distinct, if small, improvement on the *Nigers*. Very fast: 10-11kts close-hauled in a topgallant gale, and 14kts on a broad reach in a stiff gale. Remarkable performance to windward, making less than ¼ point leeway under all plain sail, and good in stronger winds. Responsive to the helm, quick in stays but rather slow to wear; good sea-boats, rolling deeply but very easily. The evidence suggests that the later ships were not quite such sparkling performers as *Lowestoffe* herself.

Based on reports on *Lowestoffe* (23 Jun 1762, 31 Mar 1763, 13 May 1773 and 29 Nov 1796); *Orpheus* (15 Aug 1773 and 17 Aug 1774); *Diamond* (19 Aug 1783).

Razée 44-gun ships, 32 guns, 1756

	Draught fwd	Draught aft	Midships port above water	Stored for service
Adventure	17ft 9in	16ft 2in	–	4 months [CS]
Sapphire	15ft 9in	14ft 8in	c7ft 4in	4 months [CS]

Probably not built to the same draught, and certainly the ships have very different sailing qualities. *Adventure*: fast off the wind, having managed 13½kts but only average close-hauled (8-9kts in a topgallant gale) and decidedly unweatherly; quick in stays; poor sea-boat, rolling quickly and considerably straining the rigging. *Sapphire*:

very good windward performance, achieving 11kts close-hauled in a topgallant gale and making only ¼ point leeway; manoeuvred well and was quick and dependable in stays; laboured when sailing large in heavy weather, and before the wind in any conditions (12kts best speed). There was obviously some distortion in her hull because she needed 25 tons more ballast to port than starboard and always carried more port weather helm than starboard.

Based on reports on *Adventure* (undated c1763 and 13 Jan 1770); *Sapphire* (8 Mar 1763).

Enterprize class, 28 guns, 1770

	Draught fwd	Draught aft	Midships port above water	Stored for service
Pegasus	16ft 1in	16ft 6in	5ft 10in	6 months [FS]
Vestal	15ft 6in	15ft 11in	6ft 6in	4 months [CS]

Not very fast: 8-9kts close-hauled and 11-12kts sailing large or running in a stiff gale is the best recorded. Rather tender – *Nemesis*, for example 'heels very suddenly to her canvas' and close-hauled sailed at too acute an angle to fight the guns easily; others would not 'bear a press of sail in any circumstances'. They were also noticeably leewardly (the angle of heel was thought to reduce the effect of the keel). Although they could not be driven hard in heavy weather, they possessed a sea-kindly hull, pitching lightly and rolling easily without straining rigging, and would 'go through a head sea easier and faster than most ships'. They were also very manoeuvrable, and would stay and wear in short compass.

Based on reports on *Enterprize* (19 Jul 1781); *Nemesis* (14 Sep 1796); *Pegasus* (2 Jan 1792); *Vestal* (19 Jul 1792 and 14 Dec 1799); *Circe* (undated c1794); *Alligator* (17 Feb 1795); *Lapwing* (3 Feb 1794).

Amazon class, 32 guns, 1770

	Draught fwd	Draught aft	Midships port above water	Stored for service
Iphigenia	16ft 3in	16ft 10in	6ft 5½ in	4 months [FS]
Castor	15ft 5in	16ft 2in	7ft 3in	3 months [CS]

Only moderately fast (11kts close-hauled in topgallant gale, 12kts on broad reach, 12½kts running) but very weatherly, and extremely manoeuvrable ('dependable in stays down to 3kts') in smooth water. A broad reach was reckoned their best point of sailing, but (exceptionally) *Amazon* claimed to have once touched 13½kts on a run. They were tender when on a bowline, which manifested itself as a high angle of heel, and they would not sail faster for being pressed, preferring a topgallant gale to heavier conditions; they sailed best when deeply ballasted. The biggest shortcoming of the class was their rough-water performance, any degree of high seas or swell adversely affecting speed, weatherliness and handling, although under reduced canvas they were easy in a seaway.

Based on reports on *Amazon* (30 Jan 1782); *Ambuscade* (19 Feb 1779); *Amphion* (10 Feb 1784); *Iphigenia* (12 Oct 1786 and undated c1795); *Andromache* (8 Aug 1786); *Castor* (15 Sep 1796); *Solebay* (11 Apr 1792 and 3 Nov 1795); *Blonde* (8 Nov 1796).

Active class, 32 guns, 1778

	Draught fwd	Draught aft	Midships port above water	Stored for service
Daedalus	16ft 6in	17ft 3in	6ft 2in	3 months [CS]

Mediocre performers in most respects, they were not very fast (best speeds being 10kts close-hauled, 11-12kts reaching and running) and were only weatherly in selected circumstances. *Daedalus*'s captain summarised his ship thus: 'The best qualities of the ship are that she brings to and steers well in a sea, stows her stores, water, provisions and complement well, sails tolerably with the wind large or in very smooth water upon a wind; in other points of view I think her a very indifferent ship...'. The consensus was that the class was very sensitive to trim, being only weatherly if trimmed deep, but on the other hand with 6 months provisions on board were too deep to sail at all fast; they were also strongly affected by a big sea, although they were easy under reduced canvas. In fact they were probably a little crank, because in a gale they seemed to sail better with less sail area. Like most British frigates, they were manoeuvrable, but somewhat slow in wearing.

Based on reports on *Daedalus* (18 Apr 1783 and 3 Jul 1784): *Active* (13 Jul 1786); *Astraea* (Feb 1784); *Ceres* (24 Feb 1784 and 9 May 1799); *Quebec* (4 Nov 1797).

Andromeda class, 32 guns, 1780

	Draught fwd	Draught aft	Midships port above water	Stored for service
Penelope	16ft 10in	18ft 4in	6ft 10in	6 months [FS]
Blanche	16ft 6in	17ft 6in	7ft 3in	3 months [CS]

An improvement over the *Actives*, in that they were far more weatherly, but they were only marginally faster (in a topgallant gale: 10kts close-hauled, 12kts with the wind on the beam, and 12½kts running). They were also stiffer in topsail weather than their predecessors, but they suffered some initial problems with stability, and correct ballasting remained critical - they needed to trim heavily by the stern, and one captain regularly moved the foremost guns right aft until enough stores in the fore hold had been consumed. They stowed their provisions adequately, with more freeboard than the *Actives*, but 6 months' victuals made them very deep, unresponsive to the helm, and sluggish. They were not at their best in high seas, but were good easy sea-boats. Their manoeuvrability was excellent in all but heavy seas.

Based on reports on *Hermione* (2 Mar 1783 and 1785); *Druid* (25 Mar 1788 and 28 Feb 1797); *Penelope* (1 Jun 1792 and 3 May 1796); *Blanche* (12 May 1792 and 10 Aug 1798).

Heldin, 28, ex-Dutch, captured 1799; sheer & profile draught taken off at Deptford Dockyard, October 1800.

Although this ship has a full quarterdeck and forecastle, the absence of any rails and a continuous gunwale gives her the appearance of a flush-decked corvette. In fact the full-height 'tween deck makes the ship high-sided even without topside barricades and it is significant that the ship was regarded as crank when close-hauled. The hull form is sharp and when sailing large the ship was moderately fast, having achieved 12kts.

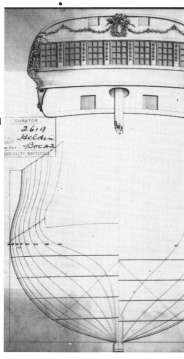

Heroine, 32 guns, 1783

	Draught fwd	Draught aft	Midships port above water	Stored for service
Heroine	16ft 7in	17ft 9in	7ft 1in	6 months [FS]

This private-venture frigate was generally the equal of contemporary official designs – not quite so fast close-hauled (9½kts in a topgallant gale) but a little faster reaching (12½kts), and was regarded as very weatherly. She handled well, stowed her provisions with ease (allowing far more freeboard to her gunports than her contemporaries) and was a good, easy sea-boat.

Based on reports of 20 Aug 1798 and 6 Mar 1802 (when armed *en flûte*).

Maidstone class, 32 guns, 1795

	Draught fwd	Draught aft	Midships port above water	Stored for service
Shannon	16ft 7in	17ft 4in	7ft 5in	6 months [FS]
Maidstone	15ft 3in	16ft 8in	8ft 4in	3 months [CS]

Only moderately fast (9kts close-hauled, 12kts reaching or running) but very stiff and good in strong winds, although their relatively high sides meant that they heeled a lot in topsail gales; for possibly the same reason, they were also a little leewardly, but it gave them unprecedented freeboard among 12pdr frigates, even when deeply stored.

Based on report on *Shannon* (25 Apr 1802).

Triton, 32 guns, 1796

	Draught fwd	Draught aft	Midships port above water	Stored for service
Triton	17ft 8in	17ft 0in	7ft 0in	? months [CS]
Triton	16ft 3in	16ft 3½in	7ft 8in	? months [CS]

It is particularly unfortunate that no Sailing Quality Report seems to have survived.

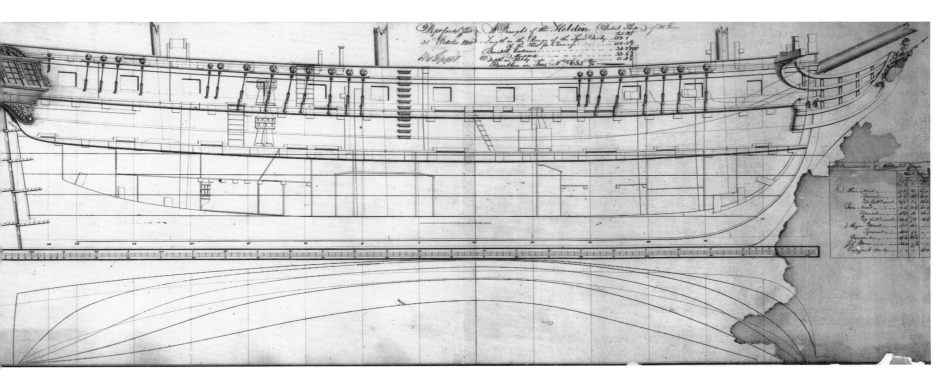

This highly experimental design was obviously regarded as a failure – given the ship's very short active career and the fact that nothing similar was built again – but it would be interesting to know in what respects the ship did not come up to expectations. Other fir-built ships had careers cut short by structural problems, but none was as curtailed as *Triton's*.

Circe class, 32 guns, 1804

	Draught fwd	Draught aft	Midships port above water	Stored for service
Circe	16ft 10in	17ft 11in	6ft 7½in	6 months [FS]
Circe	16ft 5in	17ft 10in	6ft 10½in	3 months [CS]

Compared with their prototypes, the *Richmond* class, the *Circes* were ballasted deeper and performance suffered accordingly. They were ½-1kt slower on every point of sailing (9½kts close-hauled, 11-12kts reaching and running), and although they were still regarded as reasonably weatherly, they were not outstandingly so. They were also rather crank, reducing the excellent heavy weather characteristics of the *Richmonds*. They did not stow their provisions well, and 6 months allowance was a particular problem. However, they were responsive to the helm, and quick and dependable in staying and wearing.

Based on reports on *Circe* (31 Oct 1813); *Alexandria* (7 Jan 1814); *Minerva* (22 May 1814).

Table 50: SAILING QUALITIES OF CAPTURED FRIGATES 1744-1748

See Table 49 for note on trim data; in general it is more difficult to locate this information for captured ships.

Medway's Prize, 30 guns, ex-*Favorette*, captured 1745

	Draught fwd	Draught aft	Midships port above water	Stored for service
Medway's Prize	?ft ?in	?ft ?in	?ft ?in	

Not very fast (6½kts close-hauled in a topgallant gale, 10kts reaching, 12kts running) and not very weatherly. Reasonable manoeuvrability but long in wearing. Deep but easy roller with a following wind; pitched heavily close-hauled and in a head sea 'being lean [*ie* fine-lined] forward'.

Based on report of 25 Aug 1749.

Amazon, 24 guns, ex-*Panthère*, captured 1745

	Draught fwd	Draught aft	Midships port above water	Stored for service
Amazon	12ft 0in	12ft 6in	?ft ?in	3 months [CS]

Although the ship enjoyed a reputation for fast sailing (mentioned in the initial survey and her lines were later used for a number of sloops), none of the surviving reports is very detailed. She was capable of 9½kts close-hauled in a topgallant gale and a little more in a topsail gale and had reached 13kts before the wind. She handled very well: 'not any ship under sail can steer better and stays if in trim in all seas'. She fore-reached and weathered on ships in company 'better than most', and her enthusiastic last captain claimed she 'sails the best in England', but there is no quantification by way of speeds.

Based on Reports of 9 May 1754, undated *c*1749 and 3 Sep 1763.

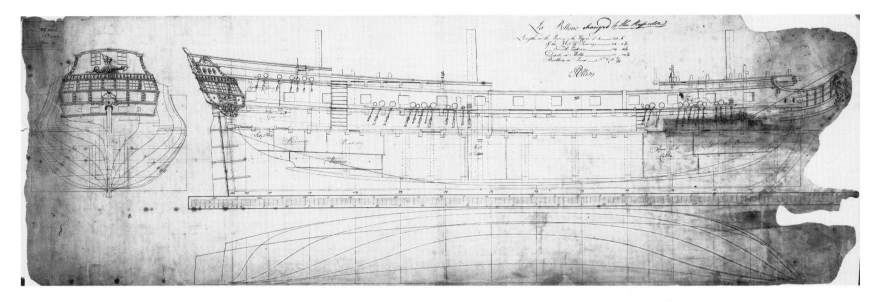

Repulse, 32, ex-French Bellone, as captured sheer and profile draught, 1759.

An extreme example of the pro's and con's of the French design style, *Bellone* was one of the fastest frigates of her day in smooth water, but was noticeably leewardly; she was also a poor sea boat.

Table 51: SAILING QUALITIES OF CAPTURED FRIGATES 1756-1763

See Table 49 for note on trim data; in general it is more difficult to locate this information for captured ships.

Repulse, 32guns, ex-Bellone, captured 1759

	Draught fwd	Draught aft	Midships port above water	Stored for service
Repulse	14ft 1in	14ft 0in	?ft ?in	6 months [FS]

Fast in smooth water (9kts close-hauled, 13kts sailing large and running), although 'very leewardly because of flat floors and small draught of water but fore-reaches'. Very much affected by sea state: 'in the trough of the sea rolls most intolerable' and even on a broad reach in a fresh gale was 'very uneasy and plunges greatly, but never to the detriment of her masts and rigging'. Manoeuvrable, but not very dependable in stays.

Based on report of 30 May 1763.

Arethusa, 32 guns, ex-Aréthuse, captured 1759

	Draught fwd	Draught aft	Midships port above water	Stored for service
Arethusa	?ft ?in	?ft ?in	5ft 10in	?
Arethusa	15ft 2in	14ft 6in	?ft ?in	? months[CS]

Fast in light conditions if not pressed (with a quartering wind had reached 12kts under double reefed topsails); quick and sure in stays but 'in veering [wearing] she requires some little time and room more than is common to English built frigates.' Mentions the ship's propensity for losing masts which the captain put down to the lack of support from the shallow hull and the excessive tumblehome; he suggested the ship was over-masted and advocating cutting down the rig.

Based on report of 19 Feb 1772.

Ambuscade, 40 guns, ex-Embuscade, captured 1746

	Draught fwd	Draught aft	Midships port above water	Stored for service
Ambuscade	15ft 9in	17ft 8in	?ft ?in	?

Relatively fast (9kts close-hauled in a topgallant gale, 12kts beam reaching, but only 11kts running); steered and wore well but would only stay properly in smooth water and was very slack in stays in a head sea. Although she would fore-reach on most ships in a calm sea, she could not weather other vessels even in smooth water and became very leewardly indeed in rougher conditions.

Based on report of 8 Apr 1761, when ship was probably past her prime.

Renown, 30 guns, ex-Renommée, captured 1747

	Draught fwd	Draught aft	Midships port above water	Stored for service
Renown	13ft 6in	14ft 2in	6ft 4in	3 months [CS]

Posssibly the fastest frigate of her day in the right conditions, the ship enjoyed a very high reputation in the French navy and was an enduring favourite in the Royal Navy. Her best points of sailing were reaching and running under reduced canvas in strong winds and smooth water (before the wind she was reckoned as fast without topgallants and stunsails as with them, and could achieve 12-13kts under double reefed topsails and fore sail with a steady gale on the beam). She had managed 13kts before the wind and the captain was convinced on the evidence of her French officers that she was good for 15kts with the wind 2 points abaft the beam – this is improbable, but indicates that the ship's speed was unusually high. Close-hauled she was only moderate 8-9kts, and in a blow was happier as canvas was taken in. She was particularly susceptible to high seas, rolling and pitching 'prodigiously', and was usually very wet being 'so low built', which also made her too stiff; she needed to be trimmed deep for best effect, which can only have exacerbated the problem. She was weatherly and manoeuvrable in smooth water, but was somewhat slow to tack and wear. By the end of her career, her speed had fallen off by about 1½-2kts on each point of sailing.

Based on reports of 13 Jul 1751 and 23 Jul 1770.

There are also extant Reports on the ex-privateers *Margate* (28 April 1749) and *Bellona* (6 Oct 1748); both seem to lack windward and heavy weather qualities, although relatively good in smooth water.

Blonde, 32 guns, ex-*Embuscade,* captured 1760

	Draught fwd	Draught aft	Midships port above water	Stored for service
Blonde	14ft 8in	14ft 10in	6ft 8in	3 months [CS]

Fast (10kts close-hauled, 11-12kts reaching, 12-13kts running) but not particularly weatherly. A good sea-boat, rolling deep but easily and behaved well even in a head sea.

Based on report of 19 Feb 1763.

Flora, 32 guns, ex-*Vestale,* captured 1762

	Draught fwd	Draught aft	Midships port above water	Stored for service
Flora	15ft 0in	15ft 0in	6ft 4in	3 months [CS]
Flora	15ft 6in	14ft 9in	5ft 6in	4 months [CS]

[The two sets of trim figures seem to contradict each other; possibly different systems of measurement were used.] Good moderate weather performance: in topgallant and topsail conditions 'little difference from our good going frigates and scarce any leeway' (8-9kts close-hauled, 12kts large), but 'under reefed topsails and courses very leewardly and seldom or ever fore-reaches on good sailing vessels', but would fore-reach with the wind right aft in smooth water. Slightly tender and regarded as over-masted in 1773. Stayed reasonably quickly but was very slow in wearing.

Based on reports of 22 Jan 1763 and 6 Feb 1773.

Brune, 32 guns, captured 1761

	Draught fwd	Draught aft	Midships port above water	Stored for service
Brune	14ft 8in	14ft 5in	5ft 8½in	3 months [CS]
Brune	14ft 11in	16ft 0in	5ft 3in	?4 months

Reasonably fast (11kts close-hauled in a topgallant gale, 12kts sailing large and running) and weatherly in smooth water. No adverse comments on her manoeuvrability but no encomiums either. Suffered from deep pitching, and in heavy weather laboured and shipped a lot of water even when lying-to. She could not stow more than 4 months' provisions. Later reports suggest that her speed had fallen significantly, particularly close-hauled.

Based on reports of about 1763 (undated), 21 Mar 1782, 1783, and 13 Jun 1792.

Aurora, 38 guns, ex-*L'Abenakise,* captured 1757

	Draught fwd	Draught aft	Midships port above water	Stored for service
Aurora	17ft 0in	16ft 10in	3ft 2in	3 months [CS]

Very fast on most points of sailing in moderate conditions (9½kts close-hauled in a topgallant gale 'in smooth water', 13kts on a broad reach and 14kts with the wind abeam; 11-12kts running). Manoeuvrable, and weatherly, except when sailing on a wind in a stiff gale with a head sea, when her sailing was 'but indifferent'.

Based on Reports of 19 Jan 1760 and an undated one of slightly earlier date.

Danae, 38 guns, captured 1758

	Draught fwd	Draught aft	Midships port above water	Stored for service
Danae	16ft 6in	16ft 0in	7ft 3in	3 months [CS]

Not outstandingly fast (10kts close-hauled in a topgallant gale, 11kts large, 9kts running are best speeds quoted, but Reports suggests a better general performance). Rather leewardly and slow in stays and wearing, but a good seaboat, pitching easiliy even in a stiff gale and head sea.

Based on report of 29 Sep 1763. There are also reports on the frigate-sized ex-French East Indiaman *Boulogne* (20 Jan 1763) and the ex-privateer *Crescent* (20 Aug 1774).

Table 52: SAILING QUALITIES OF CAPTURED FRIGATES 1776-1783

See Table 49 for note on trim data; in general it is more difficult to locate this information for captured ships.

Delaware, 28 guns, captured 1777

	Draught fwd	Draught aft	Midships port above water	Stored for service
Delaware	14ft 10in	15ft 2in	?ft ?in	? months [CS]

Not a very forthcoming report, but the ship seems to have been only moderately fast – a 'company keeper' in the phrase of the time. She recorded 7-8kts close-hauled in a topsail gale, and in general was reckoned 'on afooting with the best sailing frigates not coppered'. She could not stow the Foreign Service allocation of provisions.

Based on report of 22 Feb 1781.

Virginia, 28 guns, captured 1778

	Draught fwd	Draught aft	Midships port above water	Stored for service
Virginia	16ft 0in	16ft 6in	?ft ?in	? months [CS]

Stiff but not very fast (9kts close-hauled, 10½kts running are the highest quoted) but said to fore-reach rather than weather. In fact very leewardly under reduced canvas, and mediocre in most respects in heavy weather; best sailing 'in light winds either by or large' but 'in a stiff gale and head sea makes but little way'. Manoeuvrable.

Based on report of 25 Oct 1780.

Albemarle, 28 guns, ex-*Ménagère,* captured 1778

	Draught fwd	Draught aft	Midships port above water	Stored for service
Albemarle	15ft 9in	15ft 9in	6ft 10in	? months [FS]

Very slow (6kts close-hauled, 10-11kts reaching, 8-11kts running); 'holds a tolerably good wind but goes badly', and is particularly poor on a bowline. Stays well, but steers and wears badly.

Based on report of 7 Apr 1781.

Grana, 28 guns, captured 1781

	Draught fwd	Draught aft	Midships port above water	Stored for service
Grana	14ft 7in	14ft 7in	5ft 1in	?

Not a very detailed report but the ship could manage 11kts close-hauled and 12kts running, which was her best point of sailing. She was reckoned to be a good, easy sea-boat.

Based on report of 29 Jan 1784.

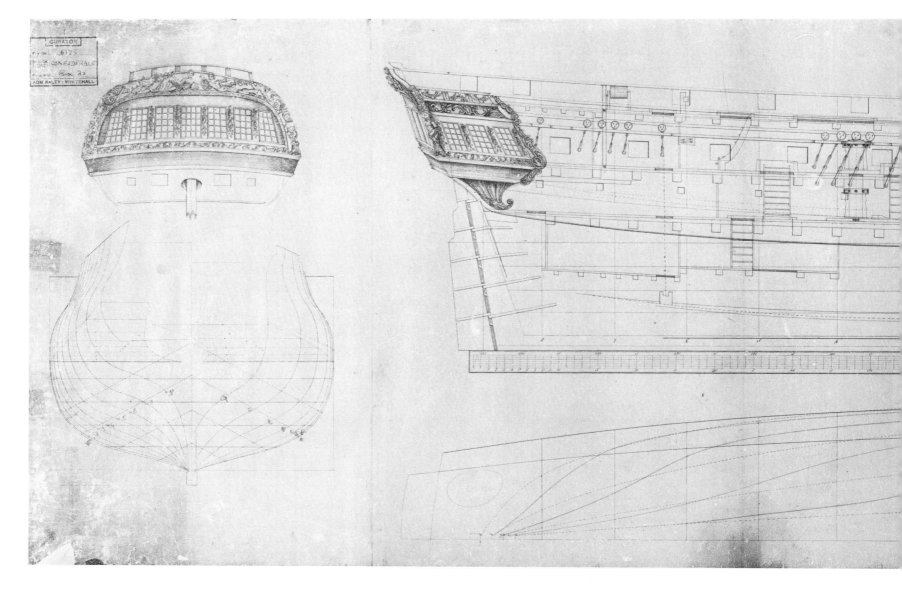

Convert (ex-*Inconstant*), 32 guns, ex-*Pallas*, captured 1778

	Draught fwd	Draught aft	Midships port above water	Stored for service
Convert	16ft 0in	16ft 4in	7ft 0in	[CS]
Convert	16ft 0in	15ft 11in	7ft 6in	?

Fast (9kts close-hauled in a topgallant gale, 12½kts running) but not weatherly: 'does not gather to windward as much as other frigates, but fore-reaches on the generality.' Stayed quickly 'in smooth water' and wore pretty well, but 'sails very indifferently in a head sea'.

Based on reports of 2 Sep 1782 and 8 Oct 1782.

Raleigh, 32 guns, captured 1778

	Draught fwd	Draught aft	Midships port above water	Stored for service
Raleigh	14ft 3in	15ft 6in	?ft ?in	? months [CS]
Raleigh	15ft 2in	16ft 4in	6ft 7in	?

Not very fast (9kts close-hauled in a topgallant gale, 11kts sailing large, 'her fastest sailing in any degree of wind'; 11kts before the wind in a hard gale) but weatherly. Manoeuvrable in smooth water but would not stay well in a head sea. Stiff, but a poor sea-boat, sailing indifferently under reduced canvas, and rolling deeply and very uneasily. Sailed best when trimmed light.

Based on report of 11 Jun 1781.

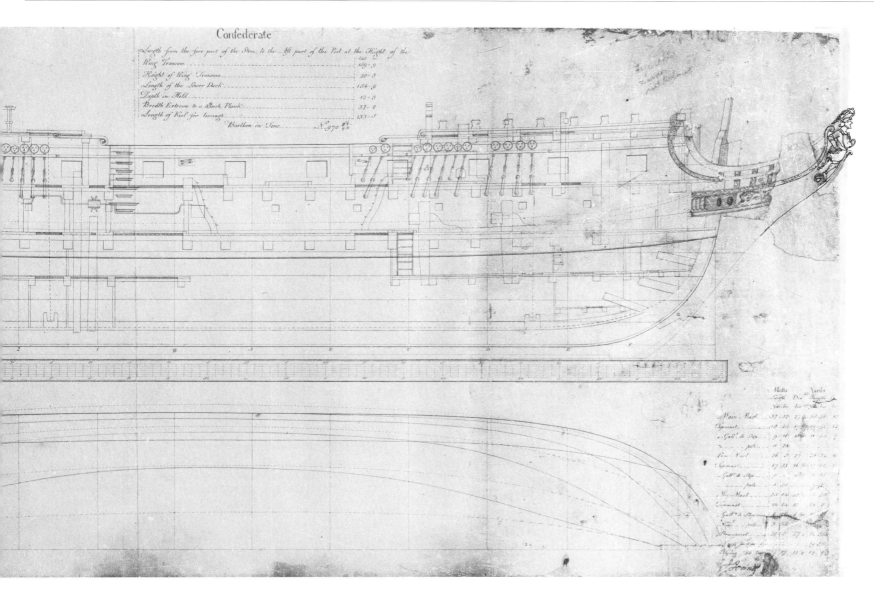

Confederate, 36, ex-American *Confederacy*, as captured sheer & profile draught 1781.

In layout this highly unusual ship was a throwback to the galley-frigates of the previous century, with a complete row of oarports on the lower deck. Nevertheless, it is worth noting that the ship did not reach the extreme proportions of French frigates like the *Oiseau*. Although an intriguing design, on survey the ship was found to be both lightly and poorly built (of unseasoned timber) and she was broken up before the end of the war.

Providence, 32 guns, captured 1780

	Draught fwd	Draught aft	Midships port above water	Stored for service
Providence	12ft 0in	13ft 0in	?ft ?in	3 months [CS]

The above is the captain's estimated best sailing trim with 3 months' provisions (she needed to be kept light for best effect and was better at 11ft/12ft). She was leewardly and would not point very high but was reckoned fast; sailing large 10kts was the best she had achieved in British service, but her original American officers claimed she had done 13kts but was spoiled by a heavy duty main mast fish applied in France. She was a good heavy weather performer, rolling easily without strain on the rigging and not pitching much; she shipped water in the waist but not over the head and forecastle. As an aside the captain said she was lightly built and would need to be repaired in the same fashion to preserve her speed; her light draught made her particularly useful in the southern American States, where she could enter virtually every important harbour, most of which were off-limits to deeper British-built frigates.

Based on a letter of 30 Oct 1780 from her captain filed with the Sailing Quality Reports.

Aimable, 32 guns, captured 1782

	Draught fwd	Draught aft	Midships port above water	Stored for service
Aimable	16ft 2in	16ft 10in	ft in	[CS]

Fast and weatherly in light conditions (9½kts close-hauled, 12½kts with the wind 1 point abaft the beam, 11kts running), and reasonably manoueuvrable: 'stays well but was never known to wear quickly'. Poor sea-boat, in heavy weather 'pitches very much, frequently carrying away topmasts, stays and backstays'; rolled deeply before the wind, but easier on her rigging.

Based on report of 2 Oct 1798.

Belle Poule, 36 guns, captured 1780

	Draught fwd	Draught aft	Midships port above water	Stored for service
Belle Poule	16ft 6in	16ft 6in	6ft 6in	? months [[CS]

Fast (10kts close-hauled, 12-13kts sailing large, 13kts before the wind) and weatherly 'when the water is tolerably smooth'. 'Proves a very fast sailer in every variation of the wind and in every strength of gale, but is considerably retarded by a great head sea.' No comments on her manoeuvrability, but in the French navy was regarded as very handy, being relatively short by their standards.

Based on report of 5 November 1782; French opinion from Jean Boudriot's monograph on the ship (p28).

Nymphe, 36 guns, captured 1780

	Draught fwd	Draught aft	Midships port above water	Stored for service
Nymphe	16ft 8in	17ft 4in	6ft 4in	? months [CS]

Fairly fast (9½kts close-hauled in a topgallant gale, 11½kts large, 12kts running) and very weatherly, but was very slow and pitched heavily in bad weather. 'Stays well but is long in wearing.'

Based on report of 15 Dec 1795.

Confederate, 36 guns, ex-Confederacy, captured 1781

	Draught fwd	Draught aft	Midships port above water	Stored for service
Confederate	16ft 0in	18ft 0in	9ft 6in	? months CS]

The surviving report is from a captain who had only had the ship for 3 months which were largely spent on convoy duty, so he felt unable to give a considered opinion. She sailed well off the wind but was best before it (although 9kts was the top speed recorded); she had done 7kts close-hauled in a topgallant gale and 8kts in a topsail gale. She was stiff but rolled a good deal, and was very poor in stays which was attributed to the fore mast being 7-8ft too far forward. This almost certainly does not represent the best the ship was capable of; the masts were later lengthened, in any case.

Based on report of 4 June 1781.

Santa Leocadia, 36 guns, captured 1781

	Draught fwd	Draught aft	Midships port above water	Stored for service
Santa Leocadia	17ft 1in	17ft 5in	6ft 3in	? months [FS]
Santa Leocadia	17ft 0in	18ft 3in	5ft 10in	? months [CS]

Fast (10kts 'or more' close-hauled in a topgallant gale, 12kts running) and very weatherly. Manoeuvrable, except in taking a long time to wear; good sea-boat, rolling quickly but easily, and pitching gently in a head sea.

Based on report of 24 Nov 1785.

Table 53: SAILING QUALITIES OF CAPTURED FRIGATES 1793-1815

Details for ships of this period are more fragmentary, with some of the records damaged, so only a small selection of reports is included. See Table 49 for note on trim data; in general it is more difficult to locate this information for captured ships.

Heldin, 28 guns, captured 1799

	Draught fwd	Draught aft	Midships port above water	Stored for service
Heldin	17ft 4in	17ft 0in	6ft 5in	?

Not very fast, the highest quoted being 12kts quartering, 10½-11kts before the wind; 6kts close-hauled in a topgallant gale when she was regarded as crank but reasonably weatherly. Stayed [tacked] well but was long in wearing.

Based on report of 25 Dec 1801.

Oiseau, 36 guns, ex-Cléopatre, captured 1793

	Draught fwd	Draught aft	Midships port above water	Stored for service
Oiseau	16ft 5in	17ft 2in	6ft 5in	[CS]

Relatively good in company but highest speed quoted is 11½kts before the wind, 9½kts close-hauled in a topgallant gale. 'Is not a weatherly ship' but steered and tacked well, although she was very slow in wearing 'owing to her great length' and required a lot of way on to perform the manoeuvre satisfactorily.

Based on report of 17 Feb 1796.

Prévoyante, 36 guns, captured 1795

	Draught fwd	Draught aft	Midships port above water	Stored for service
Prévoyante	?ft ?in	?ft ?in	?ft ?in	?

Not very fast, 11kts before the wind being the highest quoted (10kts quartering and 9kts close-hauled in a topgallant gale). She was 'generally leewardly' and although tacking easily, like so many French ships was very slow in wearing. This Report related to her last commission as a cruiser, being converted to a storeship thereafter.

Based on report of 20 Oct 1808.

12. Comparative Naval Architecture

British warship design in the age of sail has not enjoyed a good reputation, so it is worth concluding with a comparative analysis of the qualities of British frigates and those of their enemies, as seen in the many prizes taken during the second half of the eighteenth century.

DESIGN

From the period of the Establishments, the proportions of British ships tended to remain within a very narrow band (indeed all the rates of 1733 had a length:breadth ratio of 3.48, which was increased to 3.50 in 1741). Such a mechanistic approach had been given up by 1750, but the relatively short, deep hull was a feature of British cruising ships for a further forty years.

By contrast, French frigates tended to be longer in relation to breadth, and although the examples in Table 54 demonstrate the extremes, the average is well over 3.7 beams to length, compared with a British figure of less than 3.6. Perhaps more significantly, the breadth:depth ratios

reveal how shallow was the usual French hull compared to British practice. Even the relatively long *Richmond*s (which inherited a pre-Establishment tradition of hull design from the *Royal Caroline*) maintain the typically deep midship section. In fact, among the British frigates, only the *Tweed* has genuine French proportions: the classes derived from *L'Abenakise* have similar length:breadth ratios, but also retain the deeper British hull section.

During the War of Independence, the ad hoc arrangements under which the nascent American navy was designed make it unlikely that any consistent principle was at work. However, as a very broad generalisation, it is possible to see an American preference for longer ships, in the French mould, but without their extremely shallow form. *Confederacy*, which was a revival of the previous century's galley-frigate form, had atypical proportions and has to be excepted from any rule.

For the period under review there is simply insufficient evidence to make any meaningful statement about the proportions of Spanish or Dutch frigates, but by including later captures it becomes clear that the Spaniards follow the less extreme French forms whereas the Dutch are closer to the deeper British models.

Comparing the actual lines of British and foreign frigates, the French

Table 54: PROPORTIONS OF FRIGATES 1748-1785

| | | *RATIOS* | | |
	Tonnage	L:B	B:D	L:D
BRITISH CLASSES				
1748-1763				
Unicorn/Tartar, 28	583	3.56	3.31	11.79
Southampton, 32	672	3.59	2.89	10.36
Richmond, 32	646	3.74	2.89	10.81
Niger, 32	679	3.56	2.93	10.42
Tweed, 32	660	3.78	3.29	12.42
Pallas, 36	718	3.60	2.89	10.41
Lowestoffe, 32	701	3.71	2.80	10.40
Mermaid, 28	614	3.70	3.05	11.27
1770-1785				
Enterprize, 28	593	3.60	3.05	10.95
Amazon, 32	677	3.60	2.88	10.36
Active, 32	689	3.57	2.90	10.37
Andromeda, 32	710	3.65	2.75	10.05
FRENCH SHIPS				
1748-1763				
Embuscade, 40	746	3.68	3.27	12.05
Renommée, 30	669	3.63	2.99	10.86
Bellone, 32	676	3.69	3.21	11.82
Arethuse, 32	700	3.83	3.23	12.38

| | | *RATIOS* | | |
	Tonnage	L:B	B:D	L:D
Vestale, 32	699	3.81	3.31	12.24
L'Abenakise, 38	946	3.72	3.45	12.90
Danae, 38	941	3.90	3.32	12.92
1770-1783				
Oiseau, 32	784	4.29	3.44	14.78
Aimable, 32	782	3.64	3.33	12.13
Concorde, 32	888	3.81	3.24	12.34
Nymphe, 32	938	3.75	3.26	12.20
Magicienne, 32	967	3.67	3.23	11.86
AMERICAN SHIPS 1776-1783				
Delaware, 28	564	3.58	3.37	12.13
Virginia, 28	681	3.66	3.26	11.93
Hancock, 32	730	4.00	3.14	12.56
Raleigh, 32	697	3.82	3.13	11.95
Providence, 32	632	3.76	3.23	12.15
Confederacy, 36	970	4.18	3.02	12.63
SPANISH SHIPS 1776-1783				
Grana, 28	527	3.68	3.43	12.63
Santa Monica, 34	956	3.75	3.27	12.25
DUTCH SHIPS 1776-1783				
Mars, 32	703	3.75	2.94	11.05

favoured relatively sharper entrances in the fore-body and a long, fine run aft. The form varied, but the midship section also tended to be rather sharp with steeply rising floors, many adopting a characteristic two-turn bilge that came to be known as the 'French frigate form'.[78] Although this section was adopted by the British for the few ships derived from *L'Abenakise*, the round-bilge (and less typically 'French') *Tygre* hull form was far more influential. With the reservation already expressed about the circumstances of early American warship design, the Continental Navy's frigates show little sign of French influence and generally follow the more rounded British forms.

One other stark contrast between French ships and those of other nations is the enormous tumblehome of French topsides. They also tend to be lower than British or American equivalents, and display a marked reluctance to carry more than the lightest rails as quarterdeck and forecastle protection. On the other hand, until the end of the eighteenth century French frigates often carried a small poop or coach, which no British frigate ever did.[79]

Finally, it should be emphasised that the most significant difference between British ships and their opponents was one of size, British ships being small for their gun-power.[80] The reasons for this, and the significance of the contrasting design emphases, are discussed later, but first it is necessary to look at the actual structure of the ships.

CONSTRUCTION

Prizes were usually subject to a thorough survey as soon as they could be brought into a Royal Dockyard, and enough of these surveys survive to form a clear picture of French building practice. Taking French ships first, it is a remarkable feature of the surveys that the same criticisms are repeated for virtually all vessels, to the point where it is obvious that there were radically different building philosophies in operation on either side of the Channel.[81] The criticisms fall under five heads:

1. Inadequate internal arrangements. French ships usually had too few cabins, platforms in the hold, store rooms or magazines; some could not stow enough provisions and most had inadequate messing arrangements. To some extent this simply reflected different practices in the two navies (the preferred position of the magazines, for example) but the French Navy does seem to have paid less attention to the requirements of long periods at sea, and in particular to the well-being of the crew.

2. Light construction. Even the best French ships were regarded as too lightly built. The scantlings of the frames were not only heavier in British ships (typically 13in x 10in at the floors compared with 9in x 8in for similar French ships) but also more closely spaced (2½–3in as opposed to 4–7in); similarly, deck beams were further apart in French ships although sometimes slightly heavier. This lightly framed style of hull made French frigates especially vulnerable to various forms of distortion – the hogging, sagging and racking stresses common to all wooden warships – and the lack of longitudinal strength in particular

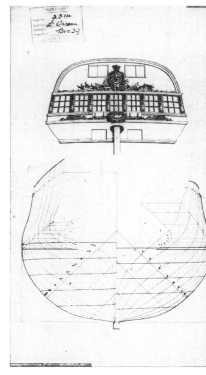

was regarded as a hallmark of French construction. Furthermore, rapid distortion was a major factor in the short operational lives of these ships, for while light building conferred advantages of speed, the better sailing qualities of such ships were quickly compromised by a hogged, broken-sheered hull.

3. Light fastening. Associated with light scantling was a general shortage of fastenings (bolts, nails or treenails), structural re-inforcements like riders, and beam knees in particular. Surveying officers were often ordered explicitly to take particular account of the fastening of French prizes and of the ironwork in general. The fundamental dislike was for the French system of attaching the beams to the side of the ship, which employed a longitudinal clamp below the beam, a rebated waterway above, and sometimes hanging knees. The strength of the beam/hull side joint decided much of the ship's transverse rigidity and also determined the weight of armament a deck could carry, and so the Royal Navy felt its system of substantially fastened hanging and lodging knees was eminently superior.

4. Shoddy building. The Royal Dockyards set very high standards – and quite frequently criticised English commercial shipbuilders – so it is not surprising to find the surveys full of references to the French use of poor materials (mainly softwoods and less durable timbers), inadequate seasoning, or dubious practices like short scarph-joints; most importantly, instead of treenails and bolts, too much use was made of iron nails, which corroded and gave rise to the condition known as 'nail-sickness'. However, many common French techniques, such as the

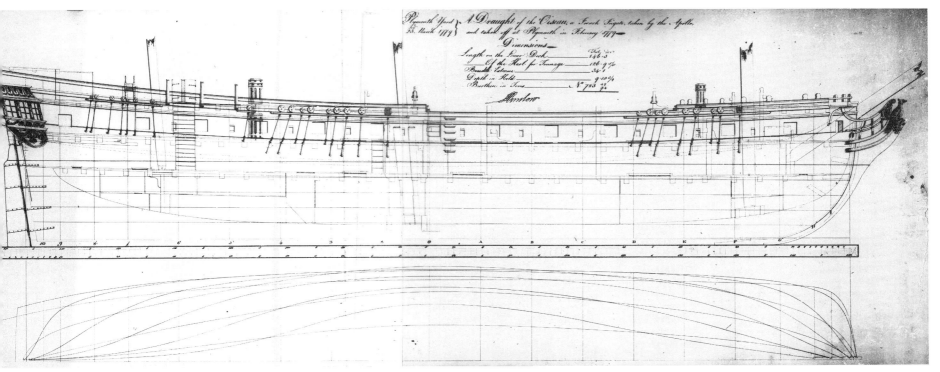

Oiseau, 32, ex-French, as captured sheer & profile draught taken off at Plymouth, March 1779.

French frigates differed significantly in their proportions from British designs: they were long in relation to breadth, but their shallow depth in hold was even more marked. (*Oiseau* was one of the most extreme with a length:breadth ratio of nearly 4.3 and a length:depth ratio of 14.8 compared with typical British figures of 3.7 and 10.5.) These proportions tended to encourage speed, but could result in leewardliness; often French frigates lacked initial stability and would not stand up under a press of sail, while the long, shallow hull would tend to flex in a seaway. When combined with lighter construction, this last characteristic tended to make French frigates prone to hogging and breaking the sheer; this meant a short service career or an expensively prolonged one.

butt-jointing of futtock timbers (as opposed to the use of scarphs and chocks), were considered shoddy, although they were probably no more than an aspect of the desire to build a hull as lightly as possible.

5. *Lack of durability.* It was a strongly held Dockyard belief that French ships were not built to last and consequently that they would be costly to maintain. Being lightly built, they would 'work' more in a seaway, opening seams and exposing the frames to wet rot and decay, making them deteriorate faster than their British equivalents. Thus they would either require more frequent and more drastic maintenance or would be quickly rendered unserviceable.

STRATEGY, TACTICS AND SHIP DESIGN

The differences of design and construction between British and French frigates are so distinctive and consistent that they must reflect official policy. Modern warships are designed to meet a series of specific performance targets in order to discharge particular roles; similar 'staff requirements', while neither so elaborate, nor as clearly articulated, must have existed for eighteenth-century navies and the only way to re-construct them is to relate the strategy and tactics to the design philosophies of each navy.

1. *Strategic considerations.* At no time in the eighteenth century could France expect to enter a war against Britain with numerical superiority, and any advantage of numbers due to alliances or strategy was too short-lived, and too uncertain, to alter the basic premise. As many an outnumbered navy has done since, the design emphasis shifted to quality

from quantity, leading those who held the purse strings to countenance larger and more costly ships of any given rate. Conversely, Britain needed the maximum number of ships and always strove for the highest practical ratio of firepower to tonnage, resulting in smaller vessels.

Superior numbers allowed the British fleet to dominate the strategic situation by controlling the seaways; furthermore the Royal Navy could defend this freedom of action by always offering battle in all but the most unfavourable circumstances. French strategists evolved a theory that the smaller French fleet should be used in support of specific objectives, and on particular missions, where they might achieve local superiority.[82] There was no question of permanently denying the use of the sea to the enemy, which had two implications: firstly, French ships needed to be fast in order to give or deny battle as circumstances dictated; and secondly, the French fleet was not expected to undertake the kind of lengthy all-weather cruising needed, for example, for blockade duty.

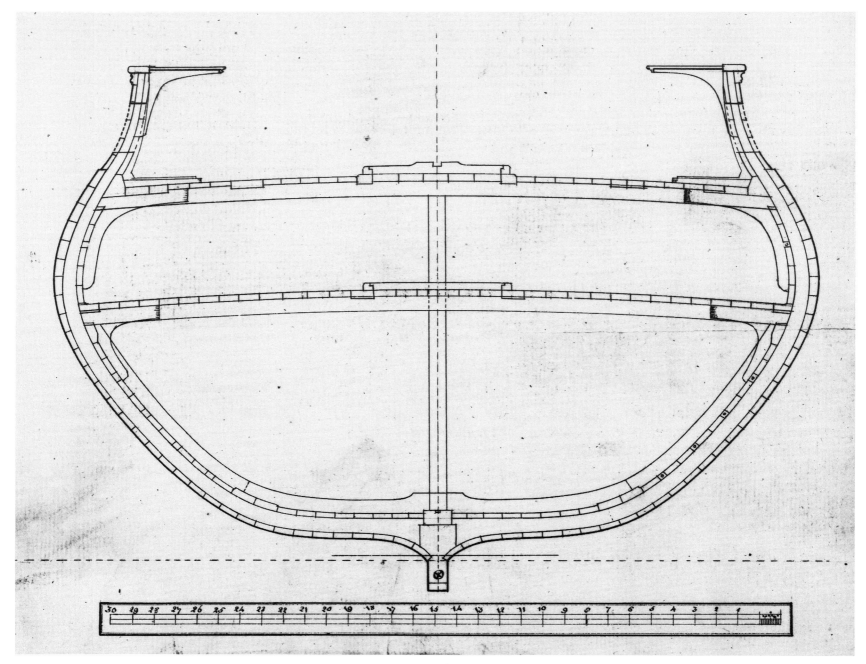

***Licorne*, 36, ex-French captured 1778; midship section.**

French warships were designed by individual *constructeurs* so series-built
classes to a single draught were rare before the 1780s. For the same reason hull
forms also varied, but the majority of frigates had a midship section based on
similar principles to this: a short floor, hollow garboards and two turns of the
bilge (one at the ends of the floors and one around the load waterline), with
extreme tumblehome of the topsides. This combined a sharp section for speed
with the ability to stow ballast and provisions as low as possible for reasons of
stability. Structure was also light, and although this section shows hanging
knees the lack of adequate support for the beam ends was a frequent complaint
of British shipwrights.

The inferiority of her battlefleets also forced France into reliance on
the *guerre de course*. With the largest merchant fleet in the world, Britain
was very vulnerable to attacks on her commerce, and for France
privateering became less a form of licensed piracy than a carefully
cultivated weapon of national policy. This emphasis left its mark on
French national frigates, which were predators *par excellence*: their speed
made them ideal for the pursuit and rapid capture of merchantmen,
while in theory they could out-manoeuvre any convoy escort; their
lighter scantling and armament were no disadvantage if one assumes

that they were not going to fight except in chosen circumstances.

While French frigates could make long cruises, it is clear that neither lengthy convoy duty, nor the rigours of blockade duty were a regular necessity. This explains why so many surveys of French prizes decry the lack of 'conveniences' – the platforms, storerooms, cabin divisions and fittings that would tend to make life slightly easier for the crew and assist in the maintenance of gear during long periods away from dockyard services. Indeed, the lower ammunition stowage, and a hull form that often made French frigates wet, lively and uncomfortable cruisers, implies that endurance was not the primary requirement.

The British stress on fighting qualities, seakeeping and independence is in direct contrast. Convoys and patrols implied months at sea, while battlefleet duty might well mean close blockade – and off the French Atlantic ports this usually meant rough water and a lee shore. In the trade protection role, British frigates were expected not only to fight off any likely assailant, but also to hunt down commerce raiders. This latter might suggest a greater emphasis on pure speed, to catch a reluctant enemy, but it has recently been calculated that the North Sea experiences wind speeds of Force 5 and above for 64 per cent of the year (Sea State 4 and upwards), while for the North Atlantic the figure is 85 per cent; the superior rough-weather performance of British frigates would give them a good chance of overhauling nominally faster ships, while their greater freeboard would allow the guns to be fought in most circumstances.

2. Tactical doctrine.
Because of the belief in the primacy of the mission, it was perfectly possible for a French commander to refuse battle without incurring official disfavour. Superior speed might be employed to escape on the ship's best point of sailing, but failing this the French had developed sophisticated defensive tactics to make the best use of the lee gage. The leeward ship would tend to heel away from its opponent, facilitating firing at masts and rigging and making it easier to dictate or break off the action; British ships, on the other hand, would probably use their superior manoeuvrability to seize the weather gage and attempt to close, where their superior firepower and better protected hulls would be at an advantage. The windward ship, heeling towards the enemy, would need to carry its guns further from the water, and the greater freeboard of British frigates' upper deck gunports is as much an indication of their firm commitment to offensive tactics as to their need to fight in all weathers.

3. Design emphases.
In crude terms, the difference between British and French frigates comes down to the relative advantages and disadvantages of a short, deep and heavily-built hull versus a long, shallow and lightly-constructed one. These may be divided into fighting and sailing characteristics.

From the point of view of fighting qualities, most of the advantages lie with the British, whose frigates ton-for-ton were superior in firepower, protection, endurance, habitability and economy of procurement. Ships of the same size would usually carry 12pdrs to the

Greyhound, Triton and Boreas of 1770, disposition of frame.

One of Sir Thomas Slade's last innovations was the introduction of a separate framing plan, of which this is one of the earliest examples. Not all the square frames are represented (the remainder duplicating the arrangement of those drawn), but it shows all the fore and aft cants, the hawse pieces and the transoms. There are two single filling frames between each doubled bend, with a single filling frame of enlarged siding in midships; the ajacent halves of the bends fore and aft of the midships filling frame are similarly sided (1ft 4in at the floor and first futtock to 1ft 1in in the toptimber according to annotations on the draught). Note also the sharp curves required of the hawse pieces.

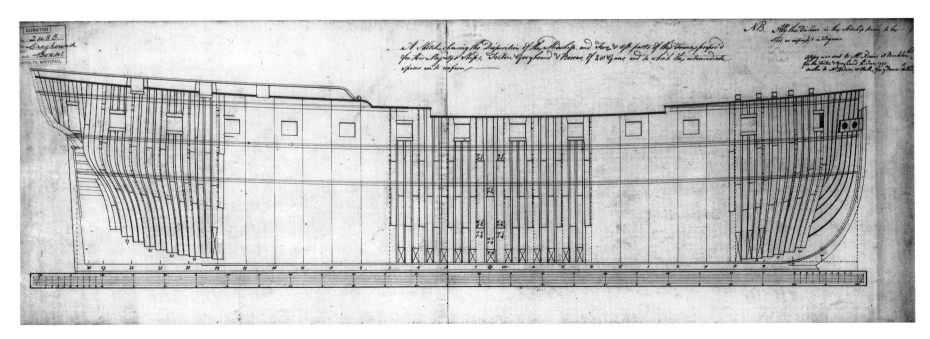

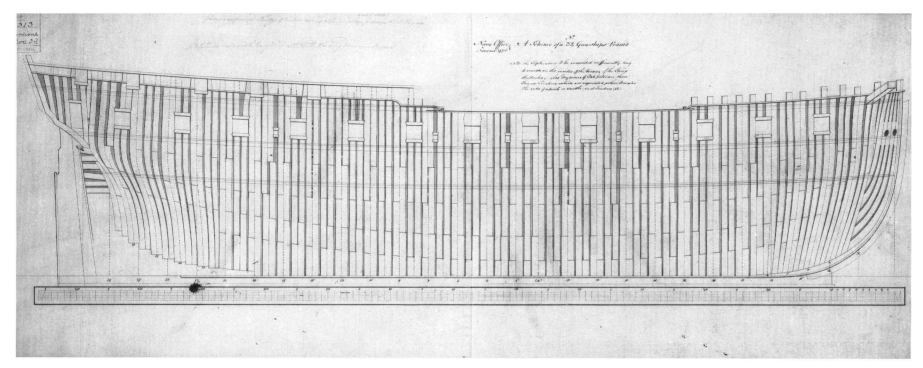

Andromeda class of 1780, disposition of frame, dated November 1779.

Framing plans soon came to show all timbers, partly because exceptions meant that even all the square frames were not identical: the fourth futtocks and toptimbers had to be offset in some places to form the sides of ports and scuttles (a note on the draught directs the toptimbers to be moulded long enough to scarph on the insides of the third futtocks when necessary) and this also involved oak spacers between elements of the framed bends. This draught is useful in portraying all space between frames as shading and this makes it clear that although the same basic pattern of two filler frames between bends is being employed, in general the siding of the topsides has been reduced somewhat. Note also that the stepping line of the forward cants has now become a curved bearding line.

French 8s (and later 18pdrs to French 12s), and because French frigates were so fine forward and allocated so much space to their captains aft, the extra length gave them no more room between gunports to fight their guns; the shallow hulls also gave them less freeboard, and a propensity to roll made them less steady gun platforms. The light scantling and almost total absence of topside protection made French ships death traps in close combat – the preferred Royal Navy tactic – and partially explains the one-sided nature of the casualties in so many single-ship engagements.

Able to stow ample provisions more readily, British frigates enjoyed a large radius of independent action, and being generally drier ships with more space between decks were more comfortable cruisers; by contrast, the shallow hulls of French frigates kept deck heights low (the gundeck was often below the waterline, so ventilation scuttles could not be cut in the sides), the internal arrangements were spartan, and since many were lively and wet sea-boats, they were not ideal for lengthy

cruising. Most significantly of all to the British, their ships were smaller so could be built in larger numbers.

With regard to sailing qualities, traditionally the advantage has been awarded to the French, and there is no doubt that the fastest ships in this study were built in France. The long hull would tend to produce greater speed, but in some ships the shallow hull also made them leewardly, and few French ships were as manoeuvrable as their shorter British opponents. British ships also exhibit better heavy weather performance, both actively in their ability to carry more sail and passively in their drier, more sea-kindly hulls. French frigates could not be matched ghosting in light airs, but in general they were not stiff enough to be driven in stronger winds.

However, the greatest disadvantage of a long, shallow hull was its propensity to distort (structurally, a deeper hull would improve girder strength and resist hogging stresses). Not only did this promote decay, but it also adversely affected performance; the Sailing Reports make it clear that ships' qualities generally declined with age, but there are many cases of ships whose hulls have been hogged in accidents (usually groundings) that never sailed as well again. So it was for many French frigates whose optimum performance was relatively short-lived; *Castor*, for example, was 'said lately to sail but indifferently' because of the state of the hull and was not purchased for the Royal Navy. Favourite cruisers like *Renown* and *Brune* had long service lives by dint of frequent and extensive repairs, but on average French frigates cost 10–15 per cent more to maintain, so British ships had a distinct advantage in economy of operation.[83]

Since we are looking at prizes through the eyes of their captors, there is some truth in the argument that the apparent shortcomings of French

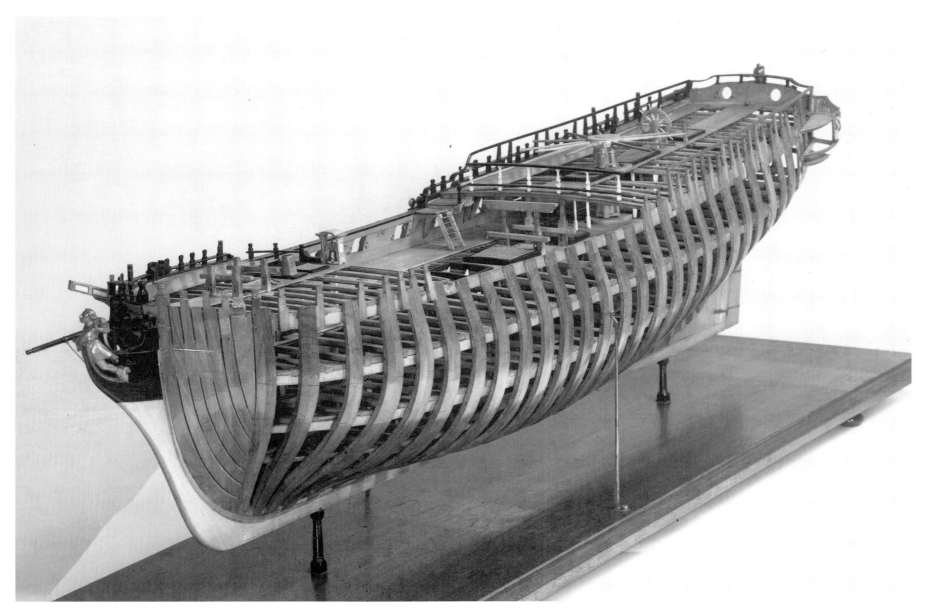

***Orpheus* of 1780, contemporary model.**

The filling frames of this model have been omitted, leaving only the bends and hawse pieces. This demonstrates how the gunports were contrived to fall between bends if at all possible, although the framing of later classes became more complex and less regular. Even so, the framing draught for this class shows the model to be a simplification, many of the bends being spaced and toptimbers offset to accommodate the various ports and scuttles.

frigates simply reflect different service requirements, and rough usage undoubtedly exacerbated their structural weakness; *Melampe*, for example, was reported 'much shattered' by her blockade duty off Brest in 1759. Although strongly disliked by dockyard officials and the Navy Board, French frigates were very popular with English naval officers and the Admiralty because their speed could make a fortune in prize money for a lucky captain, and the Admiralty regarded this as good for the service. However, the ships were not always sympathetically handled or properly understood: armament was sometimes increased, and additional weight added in the form of structural strengthening, while captains tended to drive the ships hard as they were used to doing to British frigates. In a number of cases the 'as captured' spar plan had to be reduced: in *Danae*'s case because of strain on the hull; in *Flora*'s

Triton of 1796, contemporary model.

All fir-built ships, like *Triton,* had a square tuck instead of the usual round one. There is no official explanation for this, but it was undoubtedly easier to build and may have reflected unease at the idea of steaming softwood planking to fit the subtle shape of a round tuck. Strength certainly appears to be a concern for the planking of the square tuck was specified to be oak.

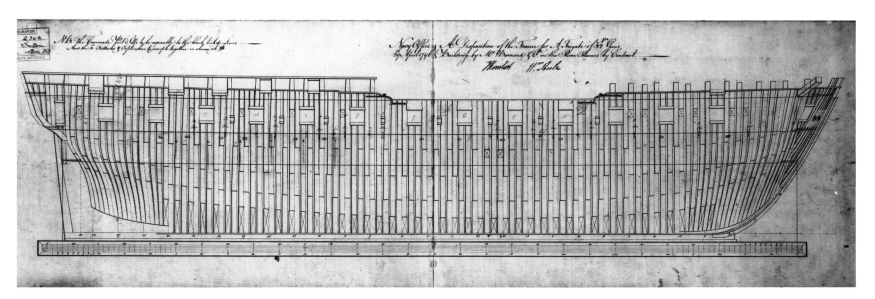

Triton of 1796, disposition of frame.

As the eighteenth century progressed the Royal Navy found it ever more difficult to obtain sufficient supplies of suitable shipbuilding timber, particularly the large naturally curved pieces used for frames. Some attempts to circumvent the problem were quite small scale: in the 1790s, for example, new methods of disposing the hawse timbers were tried in order to reduce the size and curvature of the individual pieces. In this context, it is worth noting that the contemporary *Triton*'s bow shape allowed almost straight hawse pieces to be employed (although nominally fir-built, all such ships had some hardwood elements – such as elm keel, keelson, rising and deadwood; oak stem- and sternposts, fashion pieces, apron and hawse pieces). Although built of fir, the ship's frame is otherwise conventional in its disposition.

because the captain regarded the ship as dangerously crank; and in *Arethusa*'s because the ship had a habit of rolling her masts out.

There was an element of inexperience in all this; *Arethusa*, in particular, was well known for high speed in light winds (it is mentioned in her original survey), and although she 'laboured exceedingly in bad weather' it should not have surprised the captain that after one dismasting she sailed fast under her jury rig. Similarly, *Flora*'s captain expected the ship to carry a press of sail like a British frigate, ignoring the fact that she was optimised for ghosting in light airs. Nevertheless, design characteristics contributed to all these problems. The shallow French hull gave inadequate support to the masts, while the weak structure often gave way under pressure (the *Blonde*, for instance, regularly suffered some damage to hull and rigging during chases). Because of their low sides, French frigates usually had a substantial metacentric height, which gave them good initial stability, but the excessive tumblehome reduced the righting moment at larger degrees of heel. British frigates, with deeper and broader hulls, were stiffer and could carry more sail in heavier conditions without the angle of heel that had disconcerted the *Flora*'s captain.

Table 55: COMPARISON OF WEIGHTS

| | *Renommée*, 30 | | | *Pearl*, 32 | | |
| | 669 tons bm | | | 683 tons bm | | |
	Tons	Tons	%	Tons	Tons	%
Hull		350.69	48.13		516.40	52.32
Guns	37.15			42.95		
Shot	7.33			14.40		
Powder	3.61			6.80		
Gunner's stores	3.55			9.30		
Armament		51.64	7.09		73.45	7.44
Spars	20.00			29.60		
Rigging	11.53			22.60		
Sails	4.00			6.35		
Top Hamper		35.53	4.88		58.55	5.39
Cables	12.22			24.90		
Anchors	4.78			7.35		
Ground Tackle		17.00	2.33		32.25	3.27
Boats		3.30	0.45		2.95	0.30
Sea stores	5.52			21.50		
Water	50.00			42.75		
Provisions	93.00			67.85		
Fuel	★			18.20		
Stowage		148.52	20.38		150.30	15.23
Men & Effects		22.00	3.02		23.05	2.34
Iron	?			50.00		
Shingle	?			80.00		
Ballast		100.00	13.72		130.00	13.17
TOTAL		728.68			986.95	

★ Included under 'Provisions'

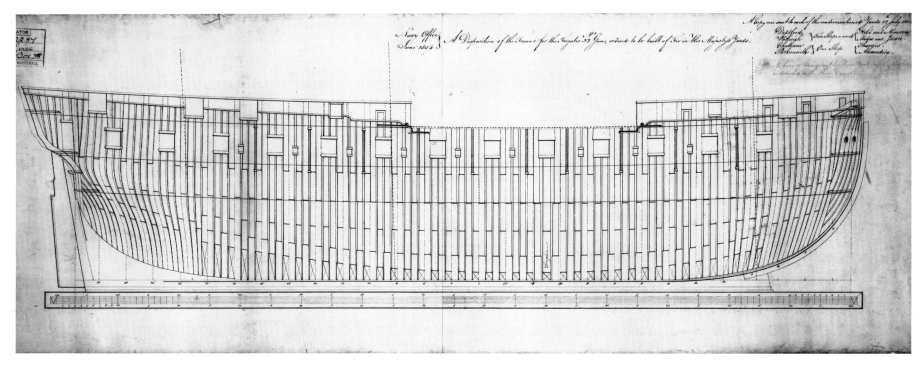

Circe **class of 1804, disposition of frame.**

The most radical approach to the timber shortage was to build ships of softwoods, a tactic that was employed as early as 1757. Although no framing plan survives for the first fir-built 28s, it is known that they were built with 'five tiers of futtocks' and it is significant that the *Circe* class adopted the same system (as did the earlier *Shannon* and *Maidstone* so this was probably standard for softwood framing). The bow design is interesting in that it requires no forward deadwood, while the hawse pieces are of a new design seated on a half timber.

As a final measure of differing priorities in ship design a comparative weight breakdown for typical French and British frigates is given in Table 55. Although both ships have similar dimensions (and hence calculated tons burthen), the heavier construction of the British ship is emphasised by her greater actual displacement and the higher proportion of that tonnage taken up by the hull. The particular emphases of British cruiser design can also be seen in the higher percentages devoted to armament (reflecting a broadside of 174lb to the *Renommée*'s 110lb French) and ammunition – *Pearl* stows twice as much powder and shot as the French ship, despite being victualled for only 3 months in this breakdown, and consequently carrying only 70 per cent of the full foreign service allowance.

The heavier top hamper reflects the traditional Royal Navy concern with all-weather performance. British frigates were expected not only to stay at sea, but also to be able to make headway in heavy weather, and accordingly required sturdy masts, spars and rigging. Much of the Sailing Quality Reports is given over to questions on how the ship lies-to,

rides to her anchor and careens, so, when the considerably more substantial ground tackle is taken into consideration, it seems clear that British frigates were designed to remain independent of shelter in most conditions. They also carried a larger proportion of sea stores, which would allow them greater endurance.

In French frigates a higher proportion of displacement was given over to provisions and consumable stores. During the course of a cruise, this would produce significant reductions in displacement and and alterations to the trim of the vessel, with possible adverse effects on the stability and sailing performance.[84] French hull design, with its emphasis on the optimum, did not respond well to these radical changes to the waterlines as the stores were consumed, but in a strategic scenario where cruises were relatively short, this was not crucial.

THE FRENCH INFLUENCE

If British and French requirements were so divergent, then why were so many French designs imitated by the Royal Navy? The short answer is that they were not: the phrase 'to the lines of' meant that the underwater hull shape was preserved, but the structure and weight distribution might be entirely different. The Admiralty went to extraordinary lengths to make *Unicorn* and *Lyme* exact 'Chinese copies' of *Tygre*,[85] because it did not trust the Surveyors of the time, but the later ships were significantly altered and, by the time the *Niger*s were designed, the lines were little more than initial inspiration.

This is clearly demonstrated by the case of *L'Abenakise*, where Slade's enthusiastic advocacy of the hull form backfired when the Admiralty ordered a series of designs from a 74-gun ship to a sloop utilising her lines. The Navy Board was forced to point out that this could not be done in any literal sense, since the proportions would mean a huge increase in the size of the battleships, which would still carry their guns too low, while the frigates would carry theirs too high and would be crank as a result.[86] The principles of the hull form could be adapted, but it is a long way from the simple scaling up or down conceived of by the Admiralty – and by many later historians.

Even today in the era of Computer Aided Design the 'previous successful ship' is still the usual starting point for a new class. If eighteenth-century British designers chose to make this a French ship, it shows neither a lack of originality nor poorer design skills.

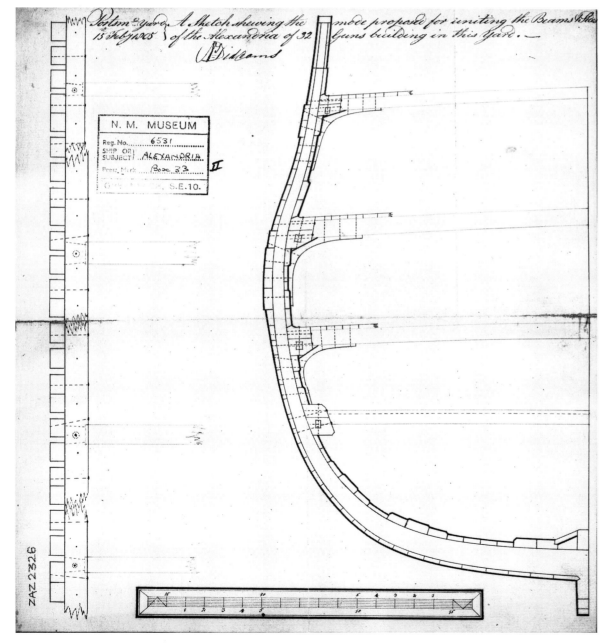

Alexandria of 1804, structural section.

As long as construction techniques were standardised, a written specification accompanying the draughts could cover the details of scantlings, fastenings and carpentry. However the drive to save compass timber produced structural experiments that required additional sketches to clarify the requirements. This draught was sent by the Portsmouth yard in February 1805 to show the Navy Board how they were intending to fasten the deck beams to the sides of this fir-built frigate. Note the dove-tailed beam ends, rebated into a thick waterway and supported with iron knees.

Notes

[1]See Brian Lavery, 'The Rebuilding of British Warships, 1690-1740', *The Mariner's Mirror* 66 (1980), pp5-14;113-27.

[2]The sloops, which were not confined by Established dimensions, were built to competing designs and tested against one another: see H I Chapelle, *The Search for Speed Under Sail* (London 1967), pp79-80.

[3]See Peter Goodwin, *The 20-Gun Ship Blandford* (London 1988), for an idea of the original layout of these vessels.

[4]The *Princesa* in particular: see Brian Lavery, *The Ship of the Line* (London 1983), vol 1, p85.

[5]In *The Rise of the English Shipping Industry* (Newton Abbot 1972), Ralph Davis estimates that about 150 ships per annum were taken in the early years, while the figure reached 500 after French entry (p317).

[6]For example, *Subtile*, survey of 27 February 1747, NMM ADM/B/135.

[7]See Jean Boudriot's monograph *La Belle-Poule 1765* (Paris 1986) for a fuller discussion of French frigate design.

[8]For examples of earlier 'frigate form' ships, see Chapter 2 of the *Line of Battle* volume (London 1992), in the History of the Ship series.

[9]See Daniel A Baugh, *British Naval Administration in the Age of Walpole* (Princeton, NJ 1965), pp251-2.

[10]NMM ADM/B/135, 27 March 1747.

[11]PRO Adm 3/57, 6 March 1747.

[12]A report in PRO Adm 106/2183, for example. This is discussed in more detail in Chapter 3.

[13]NMM ADM/B/135, 13 May 1747.

[14]Joseph Allin was appointed joint Surveyor in 1747, as a response to the Admiralty's lack of confidence in Acworth. See Baugh, *British Naval Administration*, pp89-90.

[15]See the author's 'The Frigate Designs of 1755-57', *The Mariner's Mirror* 63 (1977), pp51-69 for further details of the 20-gun ships.

[16]NMM ADM/B/155, 2 May 1757. There is no evidence that the Navy Board 'disliked the proposal', as claimed by Richard Middleton in 'Naval Administration in the Age of Pitt and Anson', in J Black & P Woodfine (eds), *The British Navy and the Use of Naval Power in the Eighteenth Century* (Leicester 1988), p115.

[17]PRO Adm 106/2183, 15 May 1747 (this is the date of the Navy Board's response, and the original report may have been submitted early enough to influence the decision to build *Unicorn* and *Lyme*).

[18]PRO Adm 95/12, 1 September 1746. The order related to the proposed construction of two 44s and two 24s in North America; only one of each, *America* and *Boston* respectively, was actually built.

[19]See Lavery, *The Ship of the Line*, vol I, pp97-9;112-3.

[20]See the author's chapter, 'Sloop of War, Corvette and Brig', in *The Line of Battle* (History of the Ship series).

[21]PRO Adm 95/29, Sailing Quality report, 23 June 1760.

[22]Built in Quebec and named after a local Indian tribe, but often misconstrued in English service as 'Bien Aquise' or 'Bon Acquise'.

[23]Even so, the long established imperative to keep down size was so ingrained that the Navy Board felt it necessary to apologise for the relatively small increase necessitated by using the *Aurora* as a model.

[24]*Letters of George III*, vol 3, p58; quoted in Lavery, *The Ship of the Line*, vol I, p106.

[25]See Howard Chapelle, *The American Sailing Navy* (New York 1959), p55.

[26]See David Syrett, 'The Failure of the British Effort in North America, 1777', in Black & Woodfine *The British Navy and the Use of Naval Power in the Eighteenth Century*.

[27]Boudriot, *La Belle-Poule 1765*, p7.

[28]There were isolated earlier examples of 18pdr frigates, but none of lasting influence: this initiative established a new norm for big frigates. See Chapter 2, *The Line of Battle* (History of the Ship series).

[29]Details in Brian Lavery, *The Arming and Fitting of English Ships of War* (London 1987), pp56-65.

[30]During his campaign against the nimble Algerine corsairs in 1679, Arthur Herbert was instructed to clean his ships at least twice every three months. PRO Adm 2/1726, 1 August 1679.

[31]She was badly damaged by grounding in 1799 and this may well have influenced the decision not to send her to sea in future; nevertheless, nothing like this hull form was ever employed again.

[32]*The Naval History of Great Britain* (London, 1860 edition), vol III, p510.

[33]The new *Tribune* class 36s were effectively copies of Hunt's *Perseverance* class of 1780 but with the contemporary solid bulwarks.

[34]See R Morriss, *The Royal Dockyards during the Revolutionary and Napoleonic Wars* (Leicester 1983), pp78-84.

[35]The sense of urgency is manifest in the Admiralty's instructions to the Navy Board, including permission to 'shoal' the best shipwrights in order to complete the ships without delay. PRO Adm 106/2234, 2 April 1804.

[36]The Dimensions Books quote 'length on the gundeck' where the draughts give 'length on the lower deck'; the main armament entry was only moved from the 'gundeck' to the 'upper deck' column from about 1795.

[37]In *Model Shipwright* 54, p89 David White argues that the term 'round bow' should be reserved for the ships with radial hawse pieces, but the looser meaning had official sanction from at least the 1740s.

[38]The author is indebted to Richard Knowles for a sketch detail of *Unicorn*'s bow based on the original draught now in the Chapman Collection in the Sjöhistoriska Museum, Stockholm.

[39]NMM ADM/B/159, 31 July 1758.

[40]PRO Adm 106/2234, 1 April 1804.

[41]PRO Adm 95/92, 17 May 1756.

[42]Some draughts of early *Niger*s show the pumps on the lower deck but the class profile notes that the Surveyor (Slade) ordered alterations including moving the pumps to the upper deck during construction.

[43]Even after the oarports were moved to the upper deck the *Richmond*s kept ten widely spaced ports on the lower deck; these are probably ventilation scuttles, but there is also what looks like a ballast port.

[44]For example, 20 June 1759 and 12 April 1781 (PRO Adm 95/93 and Adm

106/2508).

[45]PRO Adm 95/92, 9 April 1756.

[46]PRO Adm 106/2508, 27 and 29 July 1782.

[47]For more details, see Lavery, *The Arming and Fitting of English Ships of War*, pp233-5.

[48]NMM ADM/B/176, 19 June 1765.

[49]NMM ADM/B/156, 19 August 1757; PRO Adm 95/92, 22 August 1757.

[50]PRO Adm 1/428, quoted in part by W E May, *The Boats of Men of War* (Greenwich 1974), p8.

[51]NMM ADM/B/176, 19 June 1765.

[52]PRO Adm 106/2508, 19 May 1760.

[53]The order of 1773 requiring 'as completed' draughts specifically refers to carved works, so the decoration was not merely painted.

[54]PRO Adm 106/2508, 9 September 1772.

[55]PRO Adm 95/95, 6 May 1777; Adm 106/2508, 28 June 1779, 27 May 1780, 15 March 1782.

[56]PRO Adm 106/2790, 6 May 1780.

[57]Some of the early ships had a tiller on the quarterdeck and this might involve building a light grating over the tiller: *Ambuscade*, for example, PRO Adm 95/12, 21 August 1747.

[58]PRO Adm 1/4011, 12 August 1757. It did not require 12 months, since examples were ready by at least May of 1758.

[59]PRO Adm 106/2508, 19 May 1760.

[60]PRO Adm 106/2508, 29 December 1779; complaint from the captain of the *Cerberus*, 32.

[61]PRO Adm 106/2508, 19 June 1780.

[62]PRO Adm 106/2508.

[63]PRO Adm 95/93, 1 June 1779.

[64]PRO Adm 95/93, 5 February 1780.

[65]PRO Adm 106/2508, 4 October 1782.

[66]*Tartar* as fitted at Portsmouth in February 1776 carried a spar 9yds 32in long (5⅞in diam). NMM POR/D/21, 14 December 1778.

[67]PRO Adm 106/2510, 18 August 1794.

[68]PRO Adm 95/93, 12 February 1762.

[69]The related 20-gun ships utilized similar proportions and were over-sparred as a result. See NMM ADM/B/153, 28 June 1756, for the Navy Board's claim that the proportions followed those of the *Tygre*.

[70]Even *Diana*, a sister of *Southampton*, had slightly longer lower masts in December 1758, so it is quite possible that the *Richmond*s may have had their own individual spar plan. NMM POR/A/19 & 20.

[71]There is evidence that similar information was collected in a less formal fashion even earlier. PRO Adm 91/2, 8 August 1738, Surveyor's Office Letter Book contains requests from Acworth for these details.

[72]The log-line was inherently imprecise and not even standardised, varying from 42ft to 50ft between knots, but at maximum speeds of 13–14kts a 16 per cent variation is not too significant.

[73]The most cogent expression of this view is D K Brown's paper 'The Speed of Sailing Warships' delivered to the 1988 'Empires at Peace and War' conference at Portsmouth.

[74]There is evidence that the designs of both Williams and Hunt were somewhat tender and so some of the extra ballast would have been necessary even without the additional deck loads.

[75]Williams seems to have done little original design work after the mid-1770s, leaving Hunt to carry most of the burden of new design for the whole of the war.

[76]*Iris*, ex-*Hancock* had a good reputation but the evidence is entirely hearsay; those prizes for which Sailing Qualities survive appear to be no more than averagely competent sailers.

[77]Readers interested in further detail in support of this proposition are referred to the author's articles in *Petit Perroquet* 21 and 24 (in French) and a shorter English version in *Warship* 9,10 and 12.

[78]The term is misleading, since the form was widely employed throughout northern Europe from at least the late seventeenth century; a draught of the English *Sweepstakes* of 1707 is a surviving early example.

[79]See Boudriot, *La Belle-Poule*, p41, for a discussion of their history and function.

[80]The one exception was the Dutch, who continued to build small frigates. Like the British, they had considerable foreign trade to defend and over-stretched resources – particularly when at war with Britain.

[81]This section is based on the author's articles in *Petit Perroquet* 21 and 24, and *Warship* 9, 10 and 12, to which the reader is directed for further evidence to support its generalisations.

[82]See Brian Tunstall, *Naval Warfare in the Age of Sail* (London 1990), p6.

[83]See the author's article in *Petit Perroquet* 24 for for some figures on maintenance costs and longevity.

[84]This was certainly the case in the early nineteenth century: see John Fincham, *A History of Naval Architecture* (London 1851), pp255-65.

[85]It is unlikely that this was achieved since the survey of 24 March 1747 was very critical of the ship's light structure; the design dimensions of the *Unicorn*s also differed from those of *Tygre*.

[86]NMM ADM/B/164, 10 April 1760.

Sources

This book is based almost entirely on primary sources, notably the huge Admiralty Collection of draughts and official correspondence between the Admiralty, the Navy Board and officials of the Royal Dockyards. The great majority of draughts are kept at the National Maritime Museum in Greenwich and the documents at either Greenwich or the Public Records Office, Kew. The most directly relevant secondary sources are quoted in the notes to the text.

Draughts

The following is a list of plans consulted but not quite everything that is available at the National Maritime Museum (there is a drawing, for example, of an experimental steering gear fitted to *Southampton* shortly before her loss, but it is not strictly relevant to the matter of this book). Many of the draughts relate to more than one ship of the class, which over the years has lead to some variation in the exact attribution in cataloguing of the draughts; in the following list an attempt has been made to point out those that relate to the class as a whole. Greenwich has by far the most importatant collection but the holdings of other sources are also outlined.

The following abbreviations indicate the types of draught: S = sheer (lines and external appearance); P = profile (internal elevation); S&P = combined sheer and profile; Ds = decks; UD = upper deck; LD = lower deck; QD&FC = quarterdeck and forecastle; Pl = platforms; F = frame.

Admiralty Collection, National Maritime Museum

28-GUN SHIPS

Unicorn class first group
Lyme   S&P/P/Ds/Pl

Unicorn class second group
Class   S&P/After Pl/LD/UD/QD&FC
Lowestoffe   S&P
Tartar   UD&LD(1763)/S&P(1770)/Ds(1770)/S&P(1790)/ Fore Pl(1792)

Unicorn class third group
Class (as designed) S&P (*Coventry* to *Griffin*)/ LD (*Coventry, Lizard, Liverpool, Maidstone*)/ UD (*Coventry, Lizard, Liverpool*)/QD&FC (*Coventry, Lizard, Liverpool*)
(modified)   P (for all ships *Aquilon* to *Carysfort*)/S&P (*Aquilon* to *Hind*)/ Pl (*Aquilon* to *Hind*)/LD (*Aquilon* to *Hind*)/UD (*Active*)/ QD&FC (*Active*)
Coventry   Ds(1776)
Liverpool   S&P/Pl/LD/UD/Ds(1769)
Hussar   LD
Boreas   Ds(1769)
Actaeon   S&P(design)
Active   Ds(1771)
Cerberus   Ds
Argo   Ds(1775)
Milford   Ds(1775)
Guadeloupe   S&P/Ds(1770)
Carysfort   S/S&P/S&P(inc *Levant*)/P/Ds(1766)
Hind   S/P/F/Pl/LD/UD/QD&FC

Mermaid class first group
Class   S/P/Pl/LD/UD/QD&FC
Mermaid   S/Ds
Hussar   S (with *Solebay*)/P/Pl/UD/QD&FC
Solebay   Ds(1769)

Mermaid class second group
Greyhound (Class) S/P/F/Pl/LD/UD/QD&FC
Triton   S/S&P(as built)/Pl/LD/UD/QD&FC
Boreas   S&P

Enterprise class
Class   S/P
Siren/Fox   S (inc mast & spar dimensions)
Surprize   S/S&P(as built)/Ds/Pl/LD/UD/QD&FC
Enterprise   S&P/Pl/LD/LD(1787)/UD/QD&FC/QD&FC(1787)/Midsection (1787)
Actaeon   S&P(as built)/Ds
Cyclops   P/F
Rose   S/S&P(inc *Dido*)/Pl/LD/UD/QD&FC
Thisbe   Inboard planking expansion/Outboard planking expansion
Circe   S&P

32-GUN SHIPS

Southampton class
Southampton   S&P(Class)/Ds
Diana   S&P/Ds(1774)
Minerva   Ds(1770)

Richmond class
Richmond   Ds(1771)
Thames   S&P
Boston   S&P/Ds
Lark   Ds(1776)

Niger class
Class   (*Alarm*) S/P/Pl/LD/UD/QD&FC/Stern
Niger   Ds(1769)/Ds(1777)
Montreal   Ds(1768)
Emerald   S(last five ships)/LD/UD
Winchelsea   S&P)/Ds
Glory   Ds(1769)

Razée 44-gun ships
Sapphire   S

Tweed class
Tweed   Ds

Lowestoffe class
Lowestoffe   S/S&P/Pl/LD/UD/QD&FC/Ds(1769)
Diamond   S/S&P/F/Pl/LD/UD/QD&FC/Stern
Orpheus   S/S&P(as built)/F/P/Ds(1775)/Stern

Amazon class
Class (listed as *Cleopatra*) S/P/F/Pl/LD/UD/QD&FC (1810 alterations for trooping shown on the deck plans)
Amphion   S&P(as built)
Juno   S&P(as built)/P(1798)/LD(1798)/QD&FC(1798)
Iphigenia   S(inc *Success*)
Andromache   S/P/S&P(as built)/Pl/LD/UD/QD&FC

Active **class**

Class	S&P/F
Daedalus	S&P(1792)/Pl(1792)/LD/UD/QD&FC

Hermione **class**

Class	S/F/Pl/LD/UD/QD&FC/Stern
Hermione	S(inc *Druid*)/F
Andromeda	S&P(as built)

Heroine **class**

Heroine	S&P/Pl/LD/UD/QD&FC

Maidstone **class**

Pallas class	P/Pl/LD/UD/QD&FC
Maidstone & *Shannon*	S

Triton **class**

Triton	S/P/F/Pl/LD/UD/QD&FC (two versions of all except S/P)

Circe **class**

Class	S/P/F
Circe	S/P/F/Pl/LD/UD/QD&FC
Pallas	Pl/LD/UD/QD&FC
Alexandria	S&PS/P/LD/UD/QD&FC/Midship section

36-GUN CLASSES

Pallas **class**

Pallas	P (Class)/Pl/LD/UD/QD&FC
Brilliant	S (Class)/S&P/S&P (as built)/Ds (as built)

FRENCH PRIZES

Captured 1744-8

Embuscade	S/S&P (two versions)
Renommée	S&P (two versions)
Panthère	S&P

Captured 1756-63

Abenakise	Partial lines
Bellone	S/Ds(two versions)/P/Pl/LD/UD/QD&FC
Arethuse	S&P/Ds
Brune	S&P(as captured)/S&P(as repaired)/Ds/LD/UD/QD&FC
Danae	S&P(two versions)/Ds

Captured 1778-83

Ménagère	S&P/Pl/LD/UD/QD&FC
Licorne	S&P/P/Pl&LD/UD/QD&FC/Midsection
Oiseau	S&P/P/Ds&Stern/Ds/Pl/S(in 1800)
Danae	S&P/Ds
Alcmene	As captured:S&P/Pl&LD/Ds
	As fitted:Pl/LD/UD/QD&FC
Esperance	S&P
Aimable	As repaired:S/P/Pl/LD/UD/QD&FC
Prudente	S&P
Belle Poule	S&P
Nymphe	S&P
Concorde	As captured:S&P/LD/UD/QD&FC
	As repaired 1790:P/Pl/LD/UD/QD&FC
Magicienne	S&P/S/P/Pl/LD/UD/QD&FC(two or three versions of all except S&P)

Captured 1793-1815

Tourterelle	As captured:S&P/Ds
	As fitted:S/P/Ds
Unité	S&P/Ds
Cléopatre	S&P/P/Pl/LD/UD/QD&FC
Lutine	S&P/P/Pl/LD/UD/QD&FC
Réunion	S&P/Pl/LD/UD/QD&FC
Topaze	S&P/Pl/LD/UD/QD&FC/Figurehead
Atalante	S
Pique	S&P/LD/UD/QD&FC
Unité	S&P/P/Ds(two versions)
Tribune	S&P/Pl/LD/UD/QD&FC
Nereide	S&P
Decade	S&P/Ds
Embuscade	S&P
Dédaigneuse	S&P/Pl&LD/UD/QD&FC
Chiffonne	S&P/Pl/LD/UD/QD&FC
Regenerée	S&P
Franchise	S&P/Pl/Ds
Psyche	S&P/Ds

OTHER PRIZES

American

Virginia	S&P/LD/UD/QD&FC
Hancock	S&P/Ds
Raleigh	S&P/Ds
Confederacy	S&P/Pl/LD/UD/QD&FC

Spanish

Grana	As captured:S&P/Ds
	As fitted:S&P/Ds
St Monica	S&P
St Margarita	As captured:S&P
	As repaired 1791:S/P/Pl/LD/UD/QD&FC
St Leocadia	S&P
Mahonesa	S&P
Ninfa	S&P

Dutch

Mars	S&P
Heldin	S&P/LD/UD/QD&FC
Braak	S&P/LD/UD/QD&FC
Jason	S&P(1800)
Guelderland	S&P/Pl/Ds/Figurehead/Stern

Danish

Fredrickstein	S&P

Hilhouse Collection, The Science Museum

28-GUN SHIPS

Lyme	S&P
Medea/*Crescent*	S

32-GUN SHIPS

Pearl	D
Cleopatra	S/P
Syren	Ds

36-GUN SHIPS

Brilliant	UD/QD&FC

FRENCH PRIZES
Renown   S&P(as repaired)
Brune   S&P(as repaired)

Chapman Collection, Sjöhistoriska Museum, Stockholm

28-GUN SHIPS

Unicorn   S&P/LD&Pl

32-GUN SHIPS
Unidentified
  [*Niger* class] S&P
Aquilon   S/L/P/Pl/LD/UD/QD&FC/stern

Rigsarkivet, Copenhagen

28-GUN SHIPS
Lyme   S&P
Tartar   S/P
Lizard   S
Maidstone   S/P
Aurora   S

32-GUN SHIPS
Southampton   S&P
Thames   S&P
Alarm   S&P
Winchelsea   S,P & stern
Unidentified
  [*Niger* class] S
Lowestoffe   S&P
Mermaid   S/P/Ds

FRENCH PRIZES
Hermione   S
Comète   S

Documents

The surviving archival material on the eighteenth-century Royal Navy is vast, but very little of it relates to ship design and construction, and even less to what may be called procurement policy. Any sense of the 'staff requirements' that produced particular designs has to be painstakingly reconstructed from hints, chance remarks and the occasional official pronouncement; in this process the following series have been useful to a greater or lesser degree.

A. Public Records Office
Adm 1/. Admiralty In Letters
A large miscellaneous collection with many sub-series; letters from the Board of Ordnance (1/3999ff) were useful to this book.

Adm 2/. Admiralty Out Letters
Another large and varied series; includes orders and instructions to officers and ships.

Adm 3/. Admiralty Board Minutes
Records the decisions of Admiralty Board meetings but rarely gives any sense of the reasoning behind them.

Adm 7/677. Ordinance Establishments 1679-1810
A list of 'regulations relating to the guns and small arms of the ships of the Royal Navy'.

Adm 12/. Admiralty Secretary In Letters – Digests and Indexes
Lists all orders and correspondence relating to specific subjects, alphabetically arranged.

Adm 49/. Accountant General's Department
Financial in orientation, but 49/93-94 relate to the costs of shipbuilding and repair; 49/136 is a valuable digest and index of standing orders to the Dockyards 1658-1765.

Adm 91/. Surveyor's Office Letter Books
Unfortunately a fragmentary survival of the culling of Dockyard records at the turn of the century, the few volumes offer a unique insight into the workings of the design process but relate to the 1730s and 1740s only.

Adm 95/. Controller's Office Miscellanea
The most useful single series containing information on shipbuilding, the Sailing Quality Reports, Navy Board warrants for alterations and modifications to ships, details on the stowage of ships and their resulting draught and height of ports, and scantlings lists for Dockyard-built ships.

Adm 106/. Navy Board Letters
Another large and miscellaneous series, some sections are more relevant than others: Standing Orders to the Dockyards (106/2507ff); Surveyor's Office Minutes 1780- (106/2790ff); Precedent Book for Ships' Armament (106/3061); ballasting plans (106/3122).

Adm 168/. Contracts and Specifications
On loan to the National Maritime Museum. Contract specifications for merchant-built warships, listing scantlings in complete detail. Frigates represented include *Niger*, *Lowestoffe*, *Active*, *Andromeda* and *Alcmene* (for *Maidstone/Shannon*) classes.

Adm 180/. Progress and Dimensions Books
A prime source. Originally separate works, the Dimensions Books recorded the official dimensions, as designed and as built, the armament, complement, and draught to which the ship was built; the Progress Books kept details of dates and costs of construction and every piece of Dockyard work subsequently. Eventually the information in the two works was conflated.

B. National Maritime Museum
ADM/A/. Admiralty Out Letters to Navy Board
Not abstracted or indexed so difficult to find specific items or themes unless dates of correspondence are known; can be used in conjunction with ADM/B/ series.

ADM/B/. Admiralty In Letters from the Navy Board
Each volume has an abstract so easy to use; replies usually quote date of original Admiralty communication, which can then by found in ADM/A/ series. Probably the most convenient letter books from which to follow Admiralty-Navy Board business up to 1780 but thereafter documents are heavily culled and the ensuing ADM/BP/ series is virtually useless (the Navy Board's Out Letters in the PRO's Adm 106/ have to be used instead). Because ADM/B is an In Letters series, it usually includes enclosures as well, so copies of the detailed surveys of captured ships survive, for example.

POR/A/. Portsmouth Dockyard Records, Officers' Warrants from Navy Board
Instructions on specific actions relating to named ships; often includes the original enclosures with such data as mast and spar dimensions.

POR/D/. Portsmouth Dockyard Records, Officers' Reports
Includes many surveys of captured ships from the American War period (and later) not available in the ADM/BP/ papers.

USI/NM/. Navy Lists
Similar information to the Dimensions Books, but later issues quote exact armaments actually carried (including carronades); some volumes have additional technical information.

SPB/1. A Shipbuilder's Notebook
Includes full scantlings for a 28-gun ship (probably *Guadeloupe*), various mast and spar dimensions, and details of the masting of boats.

SPB/15. Letters and Naval Memoranda of Captain Edward Rotherham 1787-1830
A remarkable compilation of data relating to the construction and fitting of ships – numbers, sizes, weights and costs of most items, from sails and rigging to the precise allocation of stores for a 3-month cruise.

SPB/37a. A Shipbuilder's Notebook (John Williams)
Most information relates to the first half of the eighteenth century but it does include a list of scantlings for the fir-built 28 *Actaeon*.

Index

Page numbers in *italics* refer to illustrations